The Skye Reading Room Anthology 2013

– Island Life -

Edited by Meg Bateman

The Skye Reading Room

First published 2013 By The Skye Reading Room

www.theskyereadingroom.wordpress.com

Typeset by The Skye Reading Room in 11 point Garamond.

ISBN 978-0-9547021-2-0

A CIP record for this book is available from the British Library

For Charlotte Johnson

Thanks must go to all those who have helped in the production of this, the first, Reading Room anthology. The Reading Room is kept going by a group of hard-working volunteers, commited to the development of prose and poetry on Skye and the surrounding areas.

Thanks also to everyone who has contributed their written work and, in doing so, enabled us to produce what is, we hope you will agree, a worthy anthology.

Richard Neath and Linda Henderson.

Foreword

Islands, whether real or make-believe – Ultima Thule, Hy Brasil, Tìr nan Òg, Atlantis – have long held a fascination for writers. Their sea-girt boundaries allow them both to represent worlds in miniature where things might function differently and to be held in the imagination as an essence of something, unmediated by adjoining territories. Their very liminality between land and sea invites symbolic readings.

The work in this anthology has been gathered by the *Seòmar Leughaidh* or Reading Room, a book group in the Isle of Skye, in a net cast far beyond these shores. Competitors for the group's Baker Prize, its invited speakers and the public were asked to submit pieces reflecting on 'island life', and work from all three categories follows. Some pieces handle the beauty of sky, land and sea in moisture-laden air; others seek definition in the ever-changing light. They glimpse the wildlife of deer and eagles, and candidly inspect the human life, both native and incoming, sometimes with admiration, sometimes with frustration. Islands can become a solace or a trap for people in crisis, existential questions less avoidable than in the clutter and distraction of the market place. Entries in Gaelic remind us of the strong undertow this language still has on the culture of the Hebrides, though other islands also appear, other languages and other soils that represent discrete and possibly inaccessible parts of our experience.

The desire for a 'place of retreat on the ocean' is no new-age fashion, as the wealth of *papa*-placenames stretching between here and Iceland testifies. Though some might say the monks left their homes for penance and not for pleasure, *Navigatio Sancti Brendani* and the Voyages of the hUí Corra and of Snedgus and MacRiagla display more delight in the exotic than trepidation. And although Colum Cille left Ireland in anguish, his esteem and affection for Iona, 'though small and mean', becomes very clear. It was in the 6th and 7th centuries that such voyages were undertaken, and in the 8th century that they were written about, with full rein given to the imagination. It is clear from the diversity of material gathered in this book that islands continue to hold a special place in creativity. It is our hope that our readers will enjoy their voyage, for no man is an island …

Meg Bateman
Isle of Skye
2013

Skye Reading Room Anthology – *Island Life*

CONTENTS

the skies

defining islands

1. This Island
by Mark O. Goodwin

This island wraps
the pleats of its shore.
Resolute, rock solid,

it slants from the spit
of sand, the clamour
and claim of storms.

Its headland bowsprit
chafes and chops
at the Minch's slap.

And the marram
on the machair is combed
and spiked with salt.

Punk is its attitude
this side of the coast.
Its song scales the air

with the wing beat
of gulls. Crows swoop
over clumps of houses,

pitched like tents,
their windows open
to drink in the sky.

And we are barnacled
to this hull of land,
hulled by its beauty,

exposed and cradled.
It gives us the strength
to cross the sea.

2. **First Skye Winter**
   by Val Fellows

First Skye Winter.
Only the hedge protects
the snowdrops from the sea –
at its roots they nestle,
heads turned from the greater
whiteness advancing behind them.

3. The Commute
by Susie Southall

Wrapped in winter morning blindfold
A fog blanket flattens the weak beam,
In the lane I creep down over icy run-off
And down on the road, shapes morph into deer and
flee
The Eilean Iarmain beacon sheds thin thread vein
illuminations
Moon to the west and waning

Skirting the Sound I spin on
Through frost hollows of Duisdale,
Traversing this southern wing to its spine
And then west,
My way downs, dips, leans into bends
Rounds lochans
To sleeping Torrin
Nursing its crofts
Beneath Blà Bheinn's steaming green greatcoat
And along the Slapin shore where it narrows
Decayed with cold.

I know how this ends —

I climb, level, climb, heading into the light,
The road drops away and abruptly gives to the sea,
The ridge arcs, gabbro hewn from the broken teeth of
giants –
Looming Gars Bheinn, his ancient grey face
weathered with rime
Shining bold, bright in the rising sun.

4. **The Moving Island**
    by Deborah Moffatt

It was a desolate island, stony and bare, without trees, without grass.
On a shore without sand we ran the boat aground
and there on the boat the man of God remained, no fool he,
while we, in vigil and prayer, passed the night on the barren island.

She saw the island as she wanted it to be,
saw beauty in the silver-black water of the lochs,
in the violet-grey grasses of the bogs,
in the cold blue stone of the hill-tops,
in the amber warmth of a man's eyes,
in the bottles lining the shelf above a bar.

In the morning, after Mass, we took all we had from the boat,
the raw meat, salt for the flesh, the few necessities left to us
on our quest to find the blessed island, the promised land,
our Holy Father's will our own, our bodies in his hands.

More than a life on the island, she wanted the island to be her life,

wanted to be defined by the rocky cliffs, the pebbled shores,
the bare hills, the long winding roads, the remote bothies,
the silent men, the wind in her hair, the muddy bog at her feet,
the red-brown murk of peat staining her bare skin, drawing her in,
pulling her deep into the very heart of the island.

With the few bits of driftwood that we found scattered about the island
we built a fire and set a pot to boil, and as the flames began to rise
we felt a strange unease, the ground heaving beneath our feet,
the island moving in a great wave from one end to the other.

Perhaps she wanted too much, tried too hard. She made mistakes,
misjudged the depths, the distances, the solidity of the rocks,
the liquidity of time, the warmth of a man's eyes. Silences stretched
from one end of the island to the other; certainties slipped,

and through the bottom of a glass she saw what she
had missed –
the instability of the island, the subsidence of trust.

*Stricken with terror, we ran from the island, leaving all we had
behind,*
*crying for protection, our hearts full of doubt, our faith sorely
tested –*
*for it wasn't lost on us that our Holy Father had never left the
boat,*
*and that all along he must have known what sort of island it
was.*

As she tethered her clothes to a rope in a howling
wind,
she heard, in the distance, the music of the pipes, a
slow march,
the lop-sided beat of the retreat, and felt stray notes
falling like tears
on her face, or perhaps it was nothing but the wind
she heard,
nothing but rain on her face, the piper and his music
only a memory
she was preparing to have after she had left the island.

As we set sail, we saw the island moving away from us,

as if the island had a life of its own, a life that could
never be hers,

our poor fire still burning on the creature's scaly back,

as if it had turned its back on her, smoke rising from
the hills

the fire we had started in ignorance and desperation,

in silent reproach, as if she alone were to blame for
the damage done,

to satisfy our needs, never thinking of the harm we did,

the eroding trust, the uncertain silences, the deceptive
welcome

never imagining that God's will would one day lead us astray.

of an unstable island, the transient passions at the
bottom of a glass.

5.   **Is/land**
       by Martin Cathcart Froden

ISLAND

For years he stood still and counted the seconds between
bated breaths, between long, old waves. Held on to the
gunwale of his boat. Saw water come to kill him, recede
away. Wished the water's intent could have been more
sinister, and spent too much time not forgetting.
Unfortunately the wind beyond the break-water was very
good for his hangovers and his mate Simon knew how to
make a strong coffee and keep quiet.

LAND

In the city, far from fishing quotas and red gills flapping,
she buys onions and green beans for a soup, watches
other people kiss and go to the cinema. No need to wait
for the boat to bring ingredients, she has the world in her
hands. She has just read the note from her daughter. *Gone
to see dad. To show him Eric. See you Mon. Love, Jen.* Wonders
if she's been too hard on him, and why her daughter is
too afraid to tell her to her face where she's going. She
walks home and out of habit cooks for two. Puts one

portion in her belly, the other in Tupperware. Wraps the nice towel set she bought them as a present and settles down with a cup of instant de-caf to watch something full of glitz.

The last time he saw his wife she was busy circling ads saying 'Room for rent' in the city paper. Her calm life had become too calm and neon, premiers, shoals of people and drinks pulled her like an apple to the ground. She made a home for herself and her daughter in the city and bought a car that used to radiate money, but now looks like a drug lord's leftovers. But in a part of town that's usually dirty her car is as good as a knighthood.

They don't know each other anymore. She hasn't filed for divorce and to him it doesn't matter. His days are the same whether he's married to her or not. It's the life of a widower. She lives in a lemon yellow flat partly paid by the absent father and treacle-slow benefits. He lives on in their house, that lemon yellow too – she was once a woman with plans – but spends most of his time out on the boat. Keeps a sleeping bag there though it's only a ten-minute walk to the house.

ISLAND

As soon as he answered the phone he knew something was wrong. He put the receiver down and splashed his face with cold water. Opened a window and called her back. He thought of his torn nets. And his left-handed ways making everything seem backward. Scissors, bread knives, table tennis, love – the thing coming from his left side, the heart. He closed the window and sat down to cry. She had never called like this before and now she wanted to come and see him. Somehow he was sure she was terminally ill, but had been too afraid to ask. Instead agreed to come and pick her up from the ferry on Friday the eleventh. Then he called Simon to see if he could man the boat alone the eleventh and the twelfth.

The tenth had been nice but over-night the weather turned. The eleventh was the kind of day that cries out for something cable knitted. With the kind of rain that requires a continuous intake of coffee, or an intravenous jab of whisky. Despite this she whistles on the ferry. Hums, tastes the words of music in her headphones, but washes out the anger and transforms upset to just about right. She's nervous and happy. She's in love and she is proud of her achievement in love. With her feet up on a chair, knees-thighs-waist at the same height, she fingers the silver band that's been on her finger for two weeks and three days. She taps out the time on it with a painted fingernail. Across from her smiles a boy. His mouth full of butter, milk, sultanas, on bread and in a deep dish with cereal. The breakfast buffet on the ferry she couldn't stomach, he couldn't live without.

The ferry comes round the breakwater. Passengers leave sea for shore, the concrete expanse of water for the craggy, boulder-strewn bit of rock plonked into the middle of the sea by the hands of geology or God. Rain and waves as the erosion of stone and man, but also drink and hard work, greet them in the face of her dad, his possible in-law. Her dad, her father, with a pebble stuck in his windpipe, towers over them. Hugs her, shakes his hand, takes her bag, evaluates him to weigh no more than six or seven good salmons. Hopes he sees a degree of mettle in the boy. At least he came along, all the way from Inverness. At least he wasn't seasick.

After general inquiries about trip, health, world affairs and weather he falls silent. The young folk hold hands and he bites his tongue. His nerves are on full beam and he both regrets and is happy that he didn't have the stomach, seems they share something daughter and dad, to have a drink in the morning. Then he remembers how few hours they are here and how many thousands of hours have passed since he saw her, and launches himself into a saga. Like a ship into icy waters.

As they walk up to the house and he tries unsuccessfully to sum up his life in a few minutes. Tries to make her see she is the peak of it. All that had come before, all that was to come, is downhill either side of her. He tells her he was on boats for many years, saw this and that, women come and go, saw alcohol being drunk and destroy, men's ambition and sweat turn sour.

'All before I met your mother. After that I had concentrated on fish. Edible, sellable. Haddock and sea bream putting cornflakes and beef burgers on our little table.'

She's a gap, like a molar pulled by rusty pliers, for him. This he doesn't tell her.

'When I was a family man, I was dry, then when I suddenly wasn't a dad anymore I drowned in drink I lost my life to the sea. The life I could have had if I had studied, had I been more of a thinker, had I been a better man. I lost your mother to the sea. Then to the land on the other side of it. She went on the ferry a lot for someone who didn't have any errands in the city. When she left holding you in her arms I had only been a dad for a year, a husband for two.'

His steel capped wellies stand in the hallway. Sulking, one in a strict pose of attention, the other keeled over, showing its wedged ugly belly like a stranded sea lion. The man is busy with the kettle. The boy has stepped out for a cigarette and her dad jokes he's so scrawny he might be blown to sea, should he anchor him to the house? She smiles.

He asks her about his wife. Tries to make it sound like light conversation. 'Does she laugh these days? Does she have a boyfriend? No, no? She had a brilliant laugh your mother, still has I suppose, can't take that away from her. If only she could use it a bit more often. I've not seen her for many years now you know, but the last time I saw her, I was in the city to sign some papers, a misunderstanding with my tax band, she was so stony-faced. She had become part of the city. She delivered her sermon about absent fathers and why I couldn't see you, and as usual I conceded. I folded. I know I shouldn't have. Seeing you here, all grown up, I know I shouldn't have. I'm so sorry. But she's hard your mother. You know my dad once said about her, 'She's hewn out of

Ailsa Craig that one', you know the island that all curling stones come from. I've tried to see you but it's not been easy, and I'm not one to impose myself.

The pop of the kettle startles him, stops him and he turns to the window to rap with a knuckle at the boy huddling in the rain and wind over a fag.

'Are you both coffee drinkers?'

'Milk for me, none for him.'

The door clicks shut and Eric bows in to the kitchen.

'Well cheers, and I'm very happy to see you. To see you both.' In his nervousness he babbles. Hears himself sound like a hen, but can't stop himself. 'Here, have a biscuit.'

After coffee Eric asks if he can watch the game and daughter and dad dress to face the wind and go for a walk. A silent but good one. She slips her arm under his and he points out things she can't remember but knows of. People say hello and he shows her off, shows her the boat and she wanders back to the house to check on Eric while he changes the oil filter.

When he comes back they are lying on the sofa. Liverpool 1, Spurs 2. He decides they should go out for a meal. There's a new Indian and he's keen to see the pair as much as he can while they're here. Not sure when, or if, they plan to come back. He goes into his room to change from t-shirt to shirt. She follows him to the threshold but he doesn't hear her. As he bares his back she catches a reflection of his chest in the mirror. They lock eyes. She points to a tattoo above his heart.

'What's that one?' She knows the anchor and the flag on his arm but not this one.

'Come and see if you like.'

The tattoo is the size of a birch leaf in spring, the size of a two-year-old's palm. In fact it is the palm of a two-year-old, but the child is now seventeen. In the past, before communications broke down, his wife occasionally sent things from daughter to dad around Christmas. This was a finger-painted paper once blue-tacked onto her kitchen wall, folded into an envelope. He turned that year's bonus into a stamp of eternal proportions.

'It's your hand, darling.'

'Oh, dad.'

'You probably don't remember the painting.'

'No I don't no.'

It is a long time since she cried on his chest. Skin to skin.

Then they call for her boy and go out to sweat over Madras and Rogan Josh. Her dad tells them stories they're too young to hear, and ones she's too young to remember.

LAND

Her mum stands in a shop where they sell matches and lighters, cards and flowers, pencils, erasers, note pads and mints for those about to go on that first date, sweets and salted nuts by the kilo, envelopes, stamps and blank cassettes (for who?), cheap wrist watches and silvery key chains that will break within a year, photocopying and passport photos, and then of course the ordinary waxed vegetables and over-ripe fruits. She looks at all the things she couldn't have on the island. Things this shop is brimful of, and she feels alone. *Was this why I left? So that I could buy things, shit like this, twenty-four hours a day?* Her daughter has made a choice. A weekend long choice, nothing more, but her trip, her note on the table, is also a comment on her love for the absent father, and possibly a comment on how she was brought up. Her mum has had an almost exclusive right to her daughter for fifteen years, but now she feels that her daughter has been lured away not by one man, but two.

She's not been introduced to Eric yet. Has heard his name, but has not been invited to give her blessing, and it's been several weeks since she first noticed the ring.

She suddenly feels disgusted with the shop, her local shop that she had always liked, and the man who she had slowly made her friend. She leaves without getting any of the things she went out for: Rosé, choc mousse, twenty Mayfair.

ISLAND

On the way home from the restaurant he is bloated, sober, glad to see his daughter engaged, if not to a macho man, a providing killer whale like himself, then at least to a nice enough boy. They walk along the quay. The boy on his own, the dad holding his daughter around the shoulders. A thing he's wanted to for fifteen years. He feels they have had enough open-heart surgery talk for one day but still wants to fill the cold air with something.

'This is a song an uncle of mine sang at our wedding,' he says. This not to make them talk about their future plans, a thing they might want to stave off until the initial excitement of having one ring has subsided and the desire for a second on her finger has arisen. A train of thought has led from daughter to wife, from present to past. 'He was one of these ones, you know, that are always quiet, then at weddings they drink a bottle to themselves and demand to sing:

'*She was a woe to win*

And a pleasure to wed

A beauty all who ever saw her said

And in my old days

When I'm grey and dull

She will still warm my bed…'

'I can't remember the rest, but you get the gist, very embarrassing for us. I just thought I'd get that one out of the way.'

Once home they have missed the last ferry. He knew they would, hoped they wouldn't mind, and he rumbles around the house looking for bedclothes, and wrestles with the fold-out sofa. Tries to gauge whether he should impose any 'Not under my roof' rules and make a bed for the boy on the upstairs landing, or let them get out of their clothes together. To dissect the day and laugh about him and mark him. He hopes to pass, hopes not to walk in on anything if he needs a glass of water, hopes not to allude to anything over breakfast.

When she goes to the bathroom he sits the boy down and looks him in the eye. He asks the boy to take care of her, tells him she's the most precious thing, the only person, himself included, he cares about. The boy nods and grows ten years in four seconds, and they toast with Sprite. Shake hands formally, now more equals than before. Then, after knocking on the bathroom door and telling her he loves her and that his house is theirs too, he goes upstairs, to sleep and hope.

6. A Few Things I know About Sheep
by Juliet Lamb

The beach in the American films on television is very different. People drive there in red cars that reflect the sunshine. They park in long, hot rows of tarmac, in between men selling balloons. They lie on broad ribbons of sand and watch each other play volleyball. Behind them hotels rise, flat and glassy. Everything shines. When I go down to the beach to help my da take the sheep in, I step on a rock slick with bird poo and algae and land in seaweed up to the top of my boot. Everything smells of dead seal. I am fairly certain all this is some sort of cosmic misunderstanding.

"Come along then, Grace Kelly," says my da without sympathy.

The hills behind us are sodden and brown, and the sheep don't want to come. I lift my hood and pull my elbows in, a sheep monk. Massive and orange, my da tumbles down the cobbly sand ahead of me, heyupping with brisk claps. He is clearly complicit in the cosmic misunderstanding. I reach down and peel a strand of seaweed off my boot, along with a clump of wet sand, and cast it away from me with an excellent haughty gesture. This is completely wasted on sheep, of course.

In his other life, when we all lived in Kirkwall together, my da was a perfectly normal shipping agent. I would guess that the sheep are a midlife crisis. In those beach films, people who have midlife crises learn to play the electric guitar or have affairs or become Buddhists. As far as I know, my da has never had an affair, and he is tone-deaf. As for Buddhism, I'm not sure if it's possible to be one if you're a liberal democrat, and my father is (was?) the recording secretary for the Orkney Liberal Democrats. I should probably look up how the two relate. Anyway, a midlife crisis is one thing, but I am fairly certain that he's forgotten that I also have a life. In my early-life version, Sunday means sleeping late, birthday parties, going to the shops, watching films at the Picky Center, and takeaway with Mum. Sheep aren't involved.

They're all huddled together at the other end of the beach, where the seaweedy cobbles straggle out to a blip of shale cliff. They face my da in that way sheep have, panicked and defiant at once, like they could go either way between committing collectivesuicide or trampling the flimsy human. If I had to like one thing about sheep, it would probably be that: you never quite know what they are going to do. My da closes in on them, and they draw together, evil-eyeing him. My job is to stand here, blocking off the rest of the beach, so that when the sheep come to this point they'll have to turn and run up the hill.

They'll stay up there, eat grass, have a bunch of ugly scruffy lambs, then come back down here for the rest of the year—they only get to be normal sheep for a few months. Sort of like me, they are victims of a cosmic misunderstanding. Maybe one day they'll just evolve into selkies and have done with it.

The sheep are starting to shuffle this way. My da is still whooping like a lunatic, his claps sucked into his gloves and spit out as dull thuds, and I can only imagine they are getting sick of it. Moving back a few steps, I startle a mallie off the bank and he flips his wings and glides off, scolding me with smudgy eyes. Under my feet, the cobbles rub up against each other with a hollow, echoing scrape like grinding teeth, vibrating up through my body. It feels as uncomfortable as chewing foil. I had better stop moving.

The day is dark with near-rain. Already the beam from the lighthouse at the dock cuts through the scraggly base of the clouds overhead. The only lighthouses in American films are in the distance, and the only boats are elegant sailboats and those fast ones with huge arms sticking out the sides. They don't have big blocky drab-colored ferries, with signs inside saying No Dirty Overalls On Seats. Come to think of it, they don't wear dirty overalls, which is clearly what my da has on under his orange jacket. I do an excellently pitiable sigh and step again just to feel the stones grind. Possibly I have done something to deserve this torture. I might as well make the most of it. Suffering is meant to be good for artists. If I am ever called upon to play the wife of a drowned sailor, maybe, or a mysterious enchantress of the waters, I can channel this experience to bring depth and pathos and realism to my work. In my acceptance speech I can thank my father who, by usurping my childhood, made me the artist I am today. I am fairly certain it will be very moving.

The sheep are coming toward me now, not running, but definitely walking. Every now and then one of them checks on my da, like they still might be thinking about making a break for it. Somehow the noise of them all walking at once isn't as bad as me on my own. All the individual grating-stone noises, differently pitched, come together to make an echoing crunch like boots in snow. I crouch a little so that they won't see me and panic. From this angle we're the same height, and they look like bigger versions of the cobblestones, grey and round. A line from a school poem comes into my head: Two mingled flocks: the sheep, the rocks. I scoot back into the seaweed and stay low. My da bobs orange behind the sheep, close enough now for me to see his expression. It's funny the way he looks, concentrated, like all he can see is sheep. He bites his lip, the same as mum says I do when I'm working hard on something. I have this sudden weird feeling that the sheep are connecting us together, like they're some kind of buzzing electric wire leading from him to me.

When he gets close enough he looks at me and nods—NOW—and a shock pumps through me and pushes me up, tall and wide. "You shall not pass," I thunder, and from behind the flock I hear my da laugh. I laugh too, and it feels like I'm pulling the laughter out of the air. Wildly, the sheep roll their eyes and swivel their heads, moving in confused circles with a cacophony of grating stone. It is a moment of supreme chaos that I am fairly certain has never before been seen: humans and sheep churning, yelling, slipping on seaweed. I go down and spring up again, waving my arms. The sheep try to get past me but they can't. I am invincible, a force field. There's a whoop that sounds like my da's, but after the second one I realize it's actually me.

It must take only a few seconds of confusion before the sheep right themselves, accept the inevitable, and file up the slope and through the gap in the fence. My da springs up behind them and slams the gate. He turns to look at me, his eyes bright and wild, with his hood fallen back and the bald part of his head beaded with fog. I remember the way I used to run up and put my arms around him when he'd come home at night from his office, wooshing in with his cold overcoat and carpet smell. The thought pushes the air out of me, makes me feel tired all of a sudden. But he's waiting for something, so I raise my fist in the air and stretch out a grin.

The croft used to belong to my da's da's da's brother, who was a genuine hermit and all twisted up like that one in The Tempest. I never met him personally—he died when I was wee—but my da used to tell me stories about visiting the old man in his hut when my da was my age. He wasn't scary, according to my da, but gentle and soft, with a massive beard and a quiet voice like old shoe leather. He ate mostly sheep meat and fish he fished himself and vegetables from his garden, and he made tea out of nettle and thistles— "like salty water with dirt," says da. They would bring chocolate biscuits when they came to visit, which were supposed to be a present for Uncle Angus, although he never ate them: they were just so da and his brothers would have something to eat besides nettle tea and fishy-tasting tinned rhubarb. Sometimes, grandda and da and his brothers would help with the sheep, which is how da knew what to do with them when he moved out to the croft, I think.

It's hard to imagine my huge grandda visiting the croft house, which is peedie. Da and I fill it up. The only other things inside are one extra chair, a table, a tiny cooktop, and a fat iron stove stuffed with peat. Da's food looks funny in there, wrapped in colorful plastic, like if you put a rock poster in a Medieval castle or something. Da checks the clock and puts water on the burner for tea, while I hang my waterproofs and start packing up my overnight things. The ferry back to Kirkwall is an hour from now. My da clears his throat.

"How's mum?"

He says it casually, like he's not been waiting since yesterday to ask. My arms go stiff. Why do you always have to be the mature one when it comes to parents? I am fairly certain that's supposed to be their job. I mean to be angry, but my voice comes out small.

"How do you think?"

Da doesn't say anything else. I keep packing, slowly, so I don't have to turn around. In the American films people's parents always fight and misunderstand each other over silly things, and then they confide in their children, who have to step in and sort them out. The American films aren't much help, though, because in real life parents just get horribly quiet, or get angry with you for no reason, or get some seaweed-sheep and move off to dark little houses on poo-infested islands, and quite honestly I don't have any patience for any of them anymore. The whole idea of being a parent is that you have it sorted out, or at least you pretend to. I don't want to tell him that mum stands at the kitchen and just stares straight ahead, because what would be the point?

The kettle squeals suddenly, making me jump, and my head dislodges some sort of drying-herb-style-thing and several old pieces of paper from the rafter. Da chuckles, although it's not even the slightest bit funny. My excellent evil glare goes unappreciated due to the tea. At least there are also ginger biscuits. His food comes from the little store on the island, and it always looks sort of depressed, like it's been sitting around for a while, with saggy packaging and a thin coating of dust. Our house in Kirkwall has big windows, carpets, fuchsia bushes, a television and a trampoline. Mum bakes bread sometimes. We must have been pretty terrible to make him want to come here instead. What did we do, Da? isn't the sort of thing you can ask without whinging, though, which sort of interferes with being righteous and mature. Zipping my rucksack, I go over to the spare chair and sit. It (of course) wobbles, and I wobble it several times just to make sure he remembers. He rolls his eyes and slides the packet of biscuits across the table.

"Ferry's coming soon," I remind him, taking one. It is (of course) already broken.

"Thora..." Da starts, stops, angles his head toward his tea so that the steam fogs his spectacles. He tries again. "Thora, what does it feel like when you're acting? Don't you ever feel like you get to be somebody else, just for a moment? Like you can feel what it's like not to be you?"

I can see where this is going.

"Every day," Da continues, looking at me earnestly through the fog. "I would wake up in the morning and know that all I could do that day was go out and be the same me as every other day. Eventually I didn't want to get up any more. The idea of it was so endless, so... flat. I miss you every day, you know that. I miss your mother so much it hurts. But I have to take a break from being me. Just for a little while. Just until I can remember how to be me again. I wish you could understand."

Actually, what I said about how parents should confide in their children, like in the films? Let's forget about that. But we don't get to take a break, I think, but don't say. Instead I eat my broken biscuit chunk, swallow, and nod very slowly. "Okay, Da. I think you should probably bring me down to the pier now."

The ferry arrives bang on time and disgorges a few disoriented arrivals. From the water, it's too foggy to see where the pier begins. I think I've forgotten a time when the whole world didn't smell like soggy seaweed and dead things. The conductor, who knows me, offers a lopsided grin.

"'Bye, Da." I give him a stiff, waterproofed hug. He's looking at me so sadly, like our dog when we go out and

47

leave her home alone, so I have to say something else. "Thanks for the sheep. It was fun." As I say that I remember jumping up from the rocks, feeling the panicked steps of the sheep on the cobbles, watching my da slip and fall and jump up again with his eyes shining, and I almost think I mean it. Impulsively I reach over and hug him again. He smiles just a crack.

"What was that for?"

"For nothing. See you next week?"

He nods, but I'm already stepping onto the deck of the ferry, back to where I belong. I'm fairly certain a person can only herd so many sheep before she requires television, fish and chips, and a hot shower. Sunday isn't over yet.

the sea

7. **Invasion**
    by Alison Barr

Ropes have minds of their own.
They migrate to one another,
corkscrew across salty seas,
multi-coloured DNA spirals
congregate in bundles.
Some stranded on beaches,
brilliant Bluefire jellyfish,
long tentacles trailing.
Some, washed up swirls,
mini-galaxies
draped over black rocks.
Some, net-intact,
vibrant orange, fisherman yellow,
concertina diamond jersey patterns.
Some brittle with age, sun baked,
degraded, weathered, weakened,
at a touch breaking into powdery filaments.

Assorted lengths float around
deep sea orifices and eddies,
hang around in crisscross rope shoals.
Swirling, shifting slowly,

catching penetrating light rays.
Natural hemp, woven, spliced, pleated, knotted,
rough ends frayed like lions tails.
Nylon, chemical blue, orange, yellow,
white, polished, ends melted.
Lost overboard from moorings, nets, rigging lines,
drifting for days and decades.
Thin, thick, twisted cords, curled, snake entwined,
hitches, stopper knots, plaited.

Where do they all go in the end? To rope heaven?
To a giant universal rope brain with rope synapses
pulsing out messages like an international homing
beacon?
Universal assembly harvested from ice scattered
northern seas,
warm southern waters.
Modern art flotsam birthed from tankers, P and O's,
Nile sloops, Hebridean yachts and local fishers,
Dover to Calais Norfolk line, Mediterranean cruisers,
shiny red funnelled Cal Macs, Japanese sampans.

Big tangles washed up on beaches all over the world,
where eyes cast over them and ghost ships cast off.

8.   Hornpipes
by Ian Stephen

1. Crossing the Minch

A ridge is one line of hills
but traits betray themselves
in individual tints

as all these monochromes
are streaked by
electric cloud.

You are the goddess
of cumulonimbus
and I could be fascinated again

as the shadow of wit is across your eyes
and I know there's something like calm there, too.
but I'm also seeing the scud of dark
and know to get all vulnerable sail
to the deck fast and
brace before the sent ice hurts

and then I'll rub my unprotected ears and nose and
eyes
and blink at yet another change of sky
and know that you would take
the bravery of the solo sailor in
an area of geos and willie-waws
where the notes of pilotage
are sketchy

but I'm on the ferry
and there's snow on An Teallach
and brightness on the Coigeach stone.

It could be time
for an egg-role.

2. Not Crossing the Minch

The ferry has sailed but
if there were no other lives but ours
I'd throw off my ropes
and dart the Minch.

Strange thing how
that single skyline
is a lot of hills.

Tomorrow you'll drive into the middle
and you'll march to one named mass.

The hairs you didn't know you had
will freeze on your face
as near to white as
your hair is close to black.

I see it now as red
on a head that's facing the other way,

an opposing you,
showing how
everything could always be different

except that
the lie of the land
is what it is.

9. Lugsail from *Bluebird*

by Ian Stephen

commissioned by an Talla Solas, Ullapool, in celebration, Norman MacCaig

A whole history of repairs
in our practical articles.
The planking and
the cloth that drives it.
One man's debris
is another's material.
We get where we need to go
by short, tacking stitches
or the lope of
homeward bounders.
We can't calibrate the fade
of patches on patches.
A sail has its own memory.
We call it stretch.

10. Second Sight
by Lorn Mcintyre

Only through silence can we understand;
nothing to do with the gift of tongues.
So it was at Eoligarry, the headland
on Barra, before the ubiquitous iPod
stopped sounds that are natural,
the air polluted by the mobile phone,
an old woman, hearing the moan
of the westerly far out in the ocean,
stared mesmerised into the fire,
saw the loaded boat off Cape Cod
smashed to smithereens by the tail
of the outraged harpooned whale,
a nephew lost in the commotion,
a vision without the soundtrack
of splintered timbers, the wails
of the widowed on the shore.
It will take a fortnight before
the tragedy reaches the Hebrides,
but her keening is now done.
She walks by the peaceful sea,
gathering flotsam, a broken oar
to stoke the fire whose radiance

will form the next vision,
unlooked for, yet inevitable
before the knock on the door.

11.   The Sons of the Blind Woman
by Ian Stephen

There was a blind woman in the village of Barvas. That's
on the West Side, Isle of Lewis. A line of houses runs
down to the sea but there's no harbour. It's a surf-beach
and it's wild a lot of the time. The sands move often and
there are piles of large boulders, smooth as pebbles, from
rolling up and down with the weight of the waves.

The blind widow, she had four sons. I think she might
have lost her man to the sea. The eldest boy was the
skipper of the village boat. The Barvas men never went to
the sea until they heard that fish were running. The risks
were too high because the surf comes in so strong on the
steep beach. There's nowhere to run. You have miles of
exposed coastline, north and south.

The Siarach - the westsiders, went for the biorach,
the piked dogfish. That's fish most other folk thought
were a menace, tearing herring nets. But, on the west
sides of North Lewis, and off North Uist too, they went
out with longlines to take the biorach. They dried and
salted them. Some were cured in smoke. Some of the
preserved fish would be stored in the inner frame of a

coil of hay. When the wind blew through the haystack, the grey sharkskin wrinkled and dried too.

The word would come from Bragar, to the south, and Ballantrushall, to the north. If the *biorach* were running, the Barvas boat would take the risk and head out from the shore to the open Atlantic. But one time were all caught in a sudden squall. They didn't make it home in daylight. So the whole village was out there on the beach.

The paraffin storm-lamps could hold a flame in strong wind. They were held up in hope. Even these weak lights might help the boys find their home shore. Everyone was scanning the white line of the surf for a scrap of red sail above it.

But of course the mother of the skipper was searching with her hearing. She was listening to every wave fall back, the stones rolling away. She was hearing it all above the wind. Great round boulders being shifted and running back down the slope. She heard a sound that was different from the rest. She knew right away what it was. That poor soul let out a shout that was near a scream. She was the first to perceive that her son had come back. The shock brought her sight back to her. She saw him.

She saw her son for the first time when his body was returned to her by the seas that drowned him.

I can't say she was grateful for the gift of sight. That woman told her three remaining sons: You can do anything. Travel anywhere in the world. Do anything in the world, as long as you don't go to sea.

Her boys, next in line, were identical twins. Neither of them wanted to do anything else but go to sea. And the main activity of the fishing moved to the north. I don't think they had the heart for it in Barvas for a while to come. There was a big shift. Folk went from fishing to feed only themselves and their neighbours, to fishing for a market. There were rows and rows of ling and cod drying out along the rocks. Every geo and every small shore in North Lewis, west and east, was occupied with the wide shapes of Lewis boats. Up in Port of Ness, there were hammers tapping away at forged iron nails, sewing plank after plank of best Scottish larch.

For most of the villagers, it was the first chance of earning something. So you could get enough to eat and maybe even have a bit of choice in what you put to your mouth. You might even get hold of a few sticks of furniture. Tons and tons of best quality deep-water fish were being landed on the northern shorelines. The boats were getting bigger, up to about thirty foot long. But they still had to be light enough to launch and recover from the shores so the boats were never decked. They were open to the elements. Of course that poor widow's boys wanted to get involved like the other lads.

Their mother could be a fierce woman and no wonder. She did her best to stop them. She stopped every local skipper in his tracks. She'd seek them out, one by one, and convince them they'd never take a scale over their gunnels again if any of them took any of her boys out to sea. Remember she had the youngest fellow too. The skippers didn't know if she had the power to do that or no but they weren't taking any chances. There's a whole list of words you don't say on a boat. A whole list of circumstances that should keep you ashore if they occur when you're planning a trip out.

If any of the crew sees a minister while he's on the way to the boat – that's not a good sign. Or if someone names that creature with the long ears, the one that tastes like underground chicken.

Of course the boys found a way. The more she tried to hold them back the more desperate they were to get out to join the fishing. They both moved up north to relatives in Ness, helping out on the larger crofts. They would bring produce and a bit of money back to their mother some Saturdays. They were both kind lads. They'd make a fuss of their young brother and spoil him a bit with small presents.

Away from home, they both got a bit of experience of the sea. They had a feel for it. When you put either one on the tiller, the boat would sail as well as it could. The twins worked together well enough but rivalry is a thing you don't want in a ship of any kind. So one brother worked his way to the helm of one *sgoth Niseach* and his twin took command of another. You didn't choose to do that. You got asked. It was an informal election. The crew knew themselves who had a safe pair of hands. Who could find the fish.

There was no hiding it then. They both did well at the fishing and could hardly get their mother to accept the banknotes they pressed into her hand. And they couldn't see how she would throw herself into the jobs around the croft with a mad kind of energy whenever they were at sea. Lucky she had that one boy left, still at home. He was a great worker too.

One time the twins took their two like-vessels the forty sea miles northnortheast of the Butt of Lewis. Not for ling and not for herring but for gannets. The Nessmen go to Sula Sgeir to take the young gannets – guga - in late August, just before they can fly from the nest. The big open boats were hauled right up the rock on their own tackle, clear of the big seas. If they were wrecked you were stranded. The men huddled together in the stone bothy and worked till they dropped. Every day but Sundays for about the fortnight. And they still do all that now, much the same way, except they are landed on the rock from a motor-powered trawler.

So each of the twins was at the helm of a vessel as like to the other as they were to each other. Only the white fishing-number on its black box, painted on the side, was different. They couldn't haul the largest of the *sgoth Niseach*, up the geo on Sula Sgeir. So their boats would have been about twenty-five feet overall. Short in the keel.

That year there was a good haul. The twin boats were back in the water, within ten days of arriving in the geo, out at the rock. They were soon rising with the swell and the *guga* went sliding to them, down a wooden chute. All the weight was packed with great care and they were ready for home.

But a big northerly squall hit them when they left the rock. There was hail in it too, under big anvil clouds. The twins had been wise enough to reef right down, looking at the signs in the darkening sky. You wouldn't want to do anything but run for it, on the tack you were on. You could only keep the wind just off your stern and let her go. If you turned to face all that weather you'd get the full weight of everything. If you lowered sail so you could hoist it the other side of the mast you'd be powerless for a time as the big rollers came at you. No choice in it. As it happened, the twins had hoisted sail on different tacks and there was nothing to be done but see it through. So they were heading away from each other, the tracks diverging further and further with every minute.

These boats fairly shift in that kind of breeze, surfing on. They have a lot of buoyancy at the stern. You need every bit of it out there. They will usually rise to the steepest of seas. But even for the *sgoth Niseach*, that water that day was as much or more than most could take.

The way I heard it, each of the twins held up one hand, leaving one on the tiller. At the top of a wave. A greeting to be seen from the sister-vessel. Since it might be the last. One twin and his crew were heading for the Butt of Lewis, looking for that light. The other was hoping to see Cape Wrath.

Remember, these were the twins from the mother who lost her first son on the home shore of Barvas. She could see her twins well enough but could scarcely bear to look at either of them. Since they'd both chosen to tempt fate and let her risk that pain again.

I can tell you now, a home shore or harbour doesn't always mean safety. Port of Ness is not an easy place to get into when there's a swell on. It's boiling at the mouth and there's a sharp turn with huge incoming seas surfing in round the corner. But the twin who was looking to get his boat and crew and catch home safe knew to keep that fierce wind on his quarter, all the way. It's at the last stretch, near home, you'd be most at risk. He knew that. Everyone was calling for him to turn in.

What he did was the other thing. Their skipper, one of the twins, held her well out, to leave the lighhouse about five miles to port. So it seemed as if they were heading right out the ocean.

That way he could hold her off the worst of the confused water you always get where the tides meet at the Butt. Far enough out to stay clear of the steep waters where the long seas meet a shelving bottom. He kept her right out so they were riding the long Atlantic seas. He chose to do that rather than track down the inside of the Hebrides to the high jabble of the North Minch.

They had to run half way down the island before the wind slackened. Then the vessel sniffed her way in to West Loch Roag. The Valtos people were amazed when the *sgoth Niseach* arrived from nowhere. After all that weather. They were made welcome and given shelter. The skipper could send word up the coast to Barvas and on up north to Port of Ness. They were all in safe.

I'm sure they were able to give out some of their *guga* to the Uigeachs.

Now we have to go back to the twin who was entering unfamiliar waters. Well, he was vigilant every second. He knew that skippers in the past had sailed boats like his as far as Sule Skerry and Sule Stack to take their share of the harvest of birds, getting there before the Orkney men. So his vessel, pretty well identical to the other, could take it. He knew to keep a big clearance off Cape Wrath and to get his bow-man keep a lookout for flatter water. Point to it. He read it just right and caught a lull to sneak into long Loch Eriboll. They had to run all down the loch to find the shore. No charts. No nothing. So there they were, a *sgoth* looking for a landfall. Much the same tactic as the twin-boat that had run off on the port tack.

The *sgoth* got a thump when she landed but they were all safe. They needed a plank or two but there was a boatbuilder in nearby Durness. Likely he noted the lines to see what was similar and what was different to the boats he built himself. The skipper was able to send his words on the telegraph-wire. So they'd know in Lewis that this *sgoth* that had gone off on the starboard tack had gotten through it.

They were given generous hospitality while the repairs were being made. They were able to offer some of their own stores and of course a share of the haul of *guga*, in exchange. Before they left, with a favourable breeze, they'd learned that the other Lewis vessel had also survived.

So the twin boats both came through that night. The twins got their boats back to Port of Ness when the wind allowed. They knew to be patient and wait for suitable conditions. And they carried on with their lives. Their mother was relieved of course but she'd been through some terrible thoughts. Her own voyage. They say she could never really warm to either of her twins again, seeing what they put her through every time the boats were out.

But what about the fourth son? The youngest of her three surviving children. It's only an adventure when you talk about it afterwards. It all looked like another tragedy at the time. An event waiting to happen.

She was taking no chances at all with the young lad. She doted on him of course but she never spoiled him. He was good-looking but didn't seem to be aware of it. Considering his background, he was cheery enough. People would gather around him for the company. The whole family was like that. Good talkers but all to the point.

His mother had a fair bit of clout now – the twins were respected skippers before but they were near-enough legends after taking their crews home safe through the hail. Her own story was well known throughout the island – the blind woman from Barvas who could see again. But she tried another tack, herself, this time. She said it plain to every skipper she met.

I lost my man to the sea, she said and I lost my first son to it. My twins are out in it every day they can. Isn't that enough? I'm asking you now not to take my youngest with you. You spread the word about that.

Her youngest became an apprentice carpenter. He was good on the tools but he was restless. He needed to see something more. So it was a matter of time before he left with some mates to try his hand at the Clyde. The lad and his mother both made their way to Govan. They weren't the only Gaelic speakers there. The Barvas woman had relations in Glasgow. Her sight just wasn't good enough to drive a Singer sewing machine but she found work just the same. A new life for both of them. She never made up fully with the twins, the skippers. She still couldn't bear it when they were at sea. But there was a letter or two. A connection.

The young lad had a bad start. He was expecting to be swinging big hammers. None of that family were all that tall but they were strong, strong people for their size.

Can you hang a door? the foreman says.

Aye of course I can hang a door.

Git on wi it then.

He hung about twenty doors that day. A decent workmanlike job. He wanted to prove he could work to speed. Match the city-bred joiners.

The ganger in the bowler went crazy.

Ah asked ye to hing a door. Wan door. Can you bastardin teuchters no count tae wan. That's how it's done here. Ye take yer time. You get it perfect. No nearly perfect. Perfect. Wan man wan door wan day. Can you git that into yer heid, Teuchter?

The boy, that woman's last son, he learned. He did fine. Picked up the lingo. It was a lot easier when he understood what people were saying to him. Soon he was working up top with the best of them. You might even have seen his face in the newsreels. Launching days. When the bowlers and the bonnets all went up in the air together.

You always saw the champagne swing. Never the ambulances going in an out the gates. You've heard of danger-money. The price to pay. The boy paid the price. The boy his mother kept from the sea. He fell to the floor of a shed in Govan.

See him there amongst the offcuts, the shavings, the fag-ends. A harder landing than a wave. Hard as a beach on the west of Lewis.

But the young one was like the twins.

Hell's teeth, you're a lucky man, teuchter. Ah thought ye were a gonner.

The Barvas boy suffered a few broken ribs, a shattered ankle and a sore month off work. I don't know what went through his mother's head. No-one could tell me that. And if I don't know it, I can't tell you. Neither can I tell you what became of the twins on Lewis. We'd probably have heard if either of the twin vessels had met a sad end. So I think we can assume that each skipper made a living for himself and raised a family.

Maybe they even visited their mother and the brother who became a cabinet-maker. He walked with a limp but that didn't show in his work. He got out of the shipyards and found his own niche before there was a hundred men queuing for every job. His mother lived for a good few years and never went hungry.

The market for dried ling and cod failed. And the market for herring came and went too. So the shores of Lewis were littered with the fading shapes of neglected vessels. You won't see a village boat ready to risk the surf at Barvas shore now. But if you look out when the wave is up you'll often see surfers there. Young men and women, waiting in the shallows, like seals.

12. Storm
by Val Fellows

In the early hours: pale
iced grass, glistening stone
blue lightning sped across the sky.
The bay froze, tide paused in a whitewave.
Mountains receded, suspended as a grey backdrop.
Wild sea surged, flung itself against blackrock.
Every living thing cowered, cringed
at such unabated fury;
yet this power evokes excitement,
spins the spiral of the soul,
renewing life's energy.

13. Floodtide
by Val Fellows

Sea flooding in,
into my being
to the edge.
A white crest
through darkness
approaching.
I hear its insistence
open mind's filtering gates,
welcome the flood –
the filling,
the cleansing,
then, upon retreat,
a newly washed space
is left shining ...

14. Sea-change
by Val Fellows

I walk in water now
listening to it slop against my feet,
eddy around my ankles;
a shorewalker in the midst of a stream,
travelling seawards at the ebb.

No desire to return to land-walking:
following paths, negotiating mud –
dark, damp earth, stationary, solid.
It does not excite me as does the perpetual
movement of light, the sounds
that accompany the passage of water.
Tides erase evidence of my presence,
wash and rearrange the sand as if I had never been.

Stepping from terra firma to machair –
already a sense of salt;
this no-man's-land between earth and sea
is tidal, treacherous.
Its puddles of stinking water harbour seaweeds,
marooned crabs, feathers, shells,
its shores boast sea pinks and samphire.

Static yet changing, this undetermined zone
is the transition from land to sea;
one step signs solid to liquid.
Softness seduces –
the next step sacrifices all
that's known to unknown.

The freedom of the uncontrolled;
how soothing this slipping, sliding,
releasing from tenure.
Walking in water, seaward hurrying;
it becomes sacrilegious to plant feet –
interrupt the flow;
easier then to submit to absolution;
meld with the element –
for which gills once equipped us.

15. Archipelago
by Andy Jackson

In the eye-socket of the ocean loch,
divers in mock-rubber circle crusted hulks,
then drop into the dark to trace the rack
of ribs. I cross the strait to knock
the barnacles from clanging hulls, and talk
with comrades lying in their bottom bunks.

Even in the summertime the water's chill
is on me like a kelpie's grip. I feel
my way along the wrecks like reading Braille.
I dream of Caribbean dives, whose still,
warm shallows drift beyond my modest scale,
and so I shiver here among Norwegian krill.

In nightmares, bubbles pop and fizz inside
my veins. Limbs thrash against the tide,
my goggles bulge with rolling, sightless eyes
and pains that run as deep as I can dive.
Surfacing from sleep, I blink and drive
my lurching minibus down to the water's side.

Later, office-bound and landlocked in a place
below the surface of myself, I appraise

conditions in the markets, far from peace
amid a storm of silt. Forecast says
visibility good, but most days
it is hard to see the hand before your face.

My fathers gathered up our islands in a cran
for centuries, trawling waters well beyond
the twelve-mile limit, gathering dominion,
then watching as it dwindled and was gone.
But all fleets must one day go for scrap, or join
the scuttled cruisers at the bottom of the main.

As tickers show the fluctuating price of crude,
the glow from Flotta flickers on the tide,
lighting up a continent that lost its head,
the nations beached and lying on their side,
a crumbling archipelago imbued
with all the danger of an ocean bed.

The islands that are left are soused in brine,
stung by gales and stalked by submarine
and migrant whale. The great Atlantic stream
could drown me and not leave a sign,
but still I dive to shipwrecks I have never seen,
between the shoals of cod and contact mine.

the land

16. Sundew
by Jen Hadfield

Does this look to you
like the cusp of never and nothing
and nowhere?

It's all happening
for the first time here –
the boom-town bog rosies
and sweats out us

panhandlers,
living hand-to-mouth
or fist-to-gut.

The next invasion,
the herring run,
an oil boom,
cats'-paws on the bay,
a mild winter,
soapstone here, china clay,
a war, a wind-farm,
crab bailed over a gunwale,
summer's come –
hearsay:

encamped in the blanket bog,
we blink our insomniac
red-rubbed eyes.

Our sticky palms tarnish
with tiny flies.

17. Peat-Cutting Haikus
by Morag Henriksen

Today on the moor
I saw the bog asphodel:
Summer is on the turn.

Bog-cotton flies its fairy flag –
Staple too fine
For human fingers.

Out at the peats
The midges are drowning
In the sweat on my upper lip.

18. Island Haikus
by Kevin MacNeil

Keening geese remind
me: put Mother's Day flowers
on her grave. Pink sky.

pale moon
staring over the hills
white rose fragrance

winter morning
a pile of snow shifts
and bleats

Incense, coffee, paint.
A life passed in deep instants.
But oh, the fading.

19. The Working Day
by Drew Love Jones

You'll probably have to lift the gate a bit to pull the bolt; the hinges have sagged a little. You'll perhaps have to carry the gate to open it for the same reason. The post is almost certainly a little spongy from years of exposure to wind and weather. Back onto your machine, drive through the gate, off again, close it. Double check it's fastened properly, you don't want to be blamed for the sheep getting out.

The track is a grey scar running through the landscape, ugly but life would be harder without it. It runs higher than the floor of the strath, it's too wet in the bottom. To your left the land climbs steeply to about 500 metres, to your right, it falls another hundred or so. At its lowest point a dam holds back water for the fish hatchery, you can see the buildings in the trees down there.

As you drive, the track gets worse, the rocks larger and the burns deeper. If you're in a pick-up perhaps you'll get the odd bang from underneath as a rock contacts the sump guard. If you're on a quad, perhaps you'll pick your way carefully around. You don't want a puncture here, an hour to walk back, find another quad and tools, come back…and your day has gone. You may pass a young couple, fully kitted out in smart North Face jackets with technical looking rucksacks, boots and poles. They may be sitting on a rock, drinking from plastic bottles. You give them a cheery 'good morning' but secretly wish they were anywhere but here. You long to tell them that if you find those plastic bottles left behind then you'd like to stuff them where the sun don't shine. You see it just too much these days. No respect.

The track rises steadily as you climb towards the bealach, twisting and turning as it makes its ponderous way to the skyline. As you crest the ridge your breath is taken away. For the third time this week…and it's only Wednesday. No matter how many times you do this the view still manages to humble you. On the far side of the bay, the hill drops sheer to the sea. If it's a clear day you can see to the Outer Hebrides, if it's rough and the waves are crashing against the hill it's just as impressive. Perhaps this is a good place to stop for a swallow of coffee from your flask. The dog will almost certainly snuggle up to you in the hope of a share of your biscuit. The sounds of squabbling oystercatchers rise up to you from the bay far below. Maybe a grouse calls behind you.

Another half a mile further you pull the vehicle into your special spot, it fits almost exactly and you stash the key where you've always stashed it. Can't risk leaving it in the ignition, this track is a honeypot for walkers. Perhaps it's still and the only breath of wind is fluky and difficult to predict. Perhaps there's a reasonable Northerly blowing, that would be best for what you have in mind. Whatever the wind is doing, it's your first consideration.

It's out with your binoculars, perhaps state of the art laser range finders, perhaps your father's old pair made by Aldis or Carl Zeiss. Perhaps it's a venerable telescope by Gray and Company of Inverness. Settle back in the heather and scan the hillside before you. Take your time now and save your feet for later. A rock, a lump of moss or heather, anything is able to morph into a beast. You get a number of false starts but eventually, there, just below the scree, perfectly blended with the hillside is a bunch of hinds. They are grazing peacefully, heads to wind. As you watch heads pop up now and again. A calf has a sudden rush of blood and charges up the hill a short way, looking for a playmate, his mother looks up and you can almost imagine her thoughts 'kids, huh!'. You smile at his antics and sweep the glass over the area again, making sure you've got them all. You don't want to stumble into any you didn't spot.

As you've been glassing, your head has subconsciously started to plan a route. The first part is easy, if a bit wet. Follow the burn until that group of rocks, then it gets a bit more tricky. There's a bit of dead ground you'll need to cross, they'll still be 600 odd meters away and facing in the other direction but it will need care. Then you'll be able to duck behind that small rise and get in for a shot. If they haven't crossed the shoulder by the time you get there that is. That might be a good thing but it'll mean a longer drag.

The rifle comes out of the slip. Wood and blued steel, carrying the name of a long-gone British maker. The bolt smooth and easily worked, heaven knows, you've cycled it enough times. Perhaps not, maybe you're carrying a modern weatherproof rifle with its sound moderator, bipod and large object scope. It doesn't matter, either will do the job. The thing that matters is between your ears.

Your first step disturbs the bog myrtle and the clean, fresh smell envelops you in the wind free confines of the burn. Perhaps you didn't spend enough time on your old boots last night; you feel damp coming through almost immediately. Perhaps it's time for new ones, modern ones with a Goretex liner. Never mind, press on. The burn climb goes to plan and you ease up and over the edge just in time to see your animals' rumps pass over the horizon. Hey ho. At least it means you can take the easy route. But glass the area before you move. Just in case.

The sweat breaks as you move up towards the ridge, muscles warming and lungs starting to blow. For the thousandth time you bless the day you gave up the B&H.

You've no idea how many times you've done this but your heart rate climbs as you near the ridge line. They might only be a few meters ahead of you or they could be half a mile. There's no telling. Work a round into the chamber, perhaps something short, fat and very fast from the USA or something longer from days gone past. It doesn't matter, they all do the job.

With safety carefully applied and rifle in the crook of your arms you drag and push with elbows and toes until you can peep over the edge. Damp comes immediately through the elbows of the old army jacket, or perhaps it's a tweed sports coat that's seen a few generations. Maybe you're wearing a state of the art smock and your elbows remain dry and warm. A head shoots up as you crest, a mere 40 meters away. You freeze. A long minute passes and her head goes back down. She's not the beast you want, she's further on, about 120 metres away and looking stick thin, perhaps a high parasite burden. With infinite care, never taking your eyes from the closer beast you bring the rifle to bear. The shot is a formality; you are confident in your ability and have taken such shots a thousand times before.

She falls on the spot without a flicker. Job done. The rest of the herd mill and group. Take another? It would certainly help you reach your cull target before the snow comes. You quickly pick another poor-doer and she stumbles, moves forward a few paces and goes down. Give the others time to move away, don't give them reason to suspect a human agency. A quick check with your glasses that neither beast is moving. All looks quiet. You whistle for the dog and she come belting up, stern thrashing, eager for her role. You send her on and follow at a more leisurely pace. She finds the first beast in a frenzy of licking and leaping, she may not be the best trained deer dog, but she loves her job.

Now the work starts. With dog safely sat nearby you apply the knife. Perhaps hundreds of pounds worth of handmade steel and cherry wood, perhaps something less expensive, plastic and stainless, but just as sharp. It doesn't matter, they both work.

A while later you take out your flat piece and find a seat on a nearby rock. You are looking at layer upon layer of hills, each less distinct than the one before. In the foreground the hills, your hills, are red and gold and green. The next layer is more purple, the following ones lilac shading to grey. It brings to mind the first time you did this, the heart racing emotion, the nervousness at the shot, the exaltation and finally the sadness.

A ripping sound rouses you from the past as an eagle streaks over the ridge behind you, its wings tearing at the air as it spots you. Better get those beasts moved and into the larder so she can have her fill of the gralloch. Give the dog the crust and move on.

The fire is burning well that evening and you take your customary dram to your chair and raise a silent toast to the beasts of the hill. It's silly and perhaps it means nothing but it's something you've always done and it feels right and proper. It's the thread which connects us all, the new entrant and the hoary old timer, the young tyro and the retired colonel. The paying guest and the professional stalker. It's about respect.

20. Dòbhrain

by Suzanne Arnold

B' e latha socair geamhraidh a bh' ann
nuair a stad mi an càr ri taobh an locha,
sgàthan de bhòidhchead nam beanntan
os cionn Loch Meudal agus fodha.

Latha cho ciùin chan fhaca mi 'son greis –
adhar soilleir glan fuar,
grian a' deàrrsadh, speuran gun sgòthan.
Bha an talamh a' leigeil anail.

Ach bha gluasad ann taobh thall an locha.
An e lach a bh' ann?
Camara nam làimh, choimhead mi a-null.
'S e dòbhrain a bh' ann, na dhà dhiubh.

Bha deigh air an loch ach bhrist iad e,
a' placadaich 's a' pleadhagaich 's a' snàmh,
earbaill an àirde, 's iad a' plumadh le plubraich –
spòrs chàirdeil do chreutairean fiadhaich.

Chaidh iad fodha, ag iasgach is a' cluich,
beathaichean uisge, sùbailte slìom,
foirfe san àrainneachd ac', nàdar air leth

94

dòbhrain is uisge co-cheòlach.

Mu dheireadh thall, ruith iad thar na deighe
is laigh iad sìos air eilean beag fraoich,
dà ainmhidh sgìth, còmhla ri chèile
nan cadal sna ghrèin, taobh ri taobh.

Nam bithinn-sa math air snàmh, nam bithinn-sa nas
bige,
nam b' e creutair nàdarrach a bh' annam,
bhithinn-sa san uisge ri taobh nan dòbhran,
a' placadaich, a' pleadhagaich 's a' bristeadh na deigh'.

21.   A Sea Eagle for Mary
by Richard Neath

'The measure of a life is a measure of love and respect – so hard to earn, so easily burned' Neil Peart.

I saw your sea eagle this morning. She stole from behind a ridge like a shadow and swept away on wings too large to be real. I captured a few precious moments and then she was gone. Now, as the day falters and the sky distils from blue to peach and gold, she (for surely, she is the same bird) drifts towards the Trotternish Ridge, a black silhouette of grace and ease and power. Alone and on high, she makes her way home.

I was on my way to the croft shop when I saw Mary's eagle for the first time today; off for a loaf of granary and some of their special, extra mature cheddar. It comes from a dairy on the mainland and has a taste violent enough to crinkle my eyes into a squint. The shop is a dusty ramshackle relic with a smell that always reminds me of a derelict barn. Mrs MacGregor sits in the corner smoking strong cigarettes and occasionally reading some old paperback novel she's liberated from the charity box. She exists as if in a cloud of stoic, stubborn irreverence, her face set in a constant unchanging half-smile that says "Aye? Go on then, I dare ye…" I would put her age at somewhere around three hundred, give or take a decade. Shelves that were once cottage doors and bits of old shed now carry items both ordinary and obscure. I once saw an obviously second hand ball-cock mechanism sitting, as if the most natural thing in the world, next to packets of plain flour and cake mix. Only last year I bought a 3hp two-stroke outboard motor from her; it was in a corner leaning against a fifty-six pound bag of King Edward tatties.

I saw no more sea eagles on my journey home, or any other unfeasibly large birds for that matter. Apart from Laura MacInnes the postie. She was leaning into the back of her van, retrieving a parcel as I drove past; she seems to be constantly expanding. I waved and said "Hi". She waved back. We smiled briefly in the sunshine. I stopped at the crossroads where Angus was unloading a few scavenged logs from his ancient pick-up. The sunshine sparkled in our grey hair, two men getting to be too old to cling on to the idea of being 'late middle-aged'. We chatted; weather, tourists, the state of the roads, sheep on the roads; normal stuff. Runrig played on my car stereo as I drove. The music masked the clatter of my long-serving diesel and stirred memories in my head where they flared like embers poked in a fire.

Back at our little cottage, I sat for a while on the front step. It was a morning of sunshine and broken cloud, high and fractured, silver like shoals of herring. A morning of warmth and light breezes that scampered past and made the long grasses shudder. I kicked off my shoes and twined my old toes amongst the green stems.

"Lawn needs cutting."

"I know, I know. I'll get to it Mary, maybe tomorrow eh?"

Lewis floated in the haze, forty miles to the north, Harris closer, rambling its way south before disappearing from view behind Waternish Head. Gulls circled effortlessly, enjoying the sunshine on this fine June day and a few finches twittered amongst the hawthorn hedge, flitting out to grab a seed or two before streaking away like little brown bullets.

"You always said they reminded you of mice, hopping and scuttling around the bottom of the bushes. They always made you smile."

Mary didn't answer. I tilted my head back and got a face full of sun, squinting as though I'd just taken a great big bite of Mrs MacGregor's cheese. The warmth of the day on my skin felt like the closeness of my loved one. Small birds chattered and, in the distance the sea swayed, a huge, dark blue mass encircling the land and the lives within.

She's made the ridge, Mary's sea eagle, and disappeared against the heather and rock. I watch her all the way as she slides effortlessly through the evening sky, my mouth hanging agape, my heart aching still, after these years passed; a black shape against the sunset and a black void within.

I re-light my pipe, a snipe thrums its constant territory and the day slips away. The heather has become nothing more than dark grey lumps that sway beyond the drifting smoke. Out in the loch, silvered rings expand to nothing. On the third finger of my left hand, a gold one glints dully in the faltering light.

Our cottage is a cosy stone box, topped with slate and full of the memories of two lives lived to the full. Around every corner lies a memory nestled into the fabric of the building and its contents, in every photograph, every painting, every comfortable cushion and darkly polished surface.

Mary dragged me here nearly forty years ago when we were both young and foolish, both bursting with love and energy and hope. We were invincible, we had no fear and we were going to live forever. She was simply returning to the island where she'd been born and lived as a child and young adult; it was somewhere she knew and loved, she was coming home. The island fitted her like a pair of old slippers while I needed to wriggle my toes a little before I felt truly comfortable. So we wriggled our toes together, in unison, as one; and I gradually fell into step. A year or so passed and I no longer missed the ease of city life and convenient commerce. Endless ocean, moorland and mountains replaced my once-loved cityscape.

My previous life seemed an irrelevance.

Bloody pipe's gone out again, just as the wind's dropped and the little biting bastards have begun to mount an attack. I re-light and puff out a thick fog of smoke to keep them at bay. I should be casting now, in this half-light, searching for the odd fish picking off the last of the hatch, but I've had my fill today. And anyway, the evening is too beautiful, too calm and too utterly perfect to spoil with any activity more strenuous than sucking on a pipe of smouldering tobacco, taking in the serenity of the view and remembering Mary.

She always hated my pipe.

At the front of the cottage, beneath one of the small front windows is an old wooden bench. We would sit and drink coffee or, sometimes, in the evening, a dram or two. I'd sit upwind of her and smoke, wafting any wayward wisps away with one hand while stroking the back of her neck with the other. We would watch the day drift into the night. Young middle age by then, settled, comfortable, content. My joints still worked and Mary's heart still pumped, just as it should. We were happy. Life was good, the cottage was the perfect home and the island was the whole world to us.

We originally thought it was a buzzard. It was a perfect silhouette on a perfect June evening and was in fact, way out, over the coast and not, as we'd first thought, over the croft. We watched, silent, stunned and aghast as this huge beast of a bird flapped its way towards us on wings that seemed out of proportion and slightly comical. She sped up as she approached and we heard the distinct rustle of the wind in her feathers; saw the wedge of white tail and curve of her yellow beak. She was our very first, a tourist from Wester Ross - a trailblazer. That was nearly twenty years ago; we were both amazed and elated, but Mary fell instantly in love.

The air is growing cool as the sun slips further away but my pipe is glowing again and my coffee is warm. I'll ache tomorrow, sitting on this damp moss. I should know better at my age I suppose, but the sense of freedom out here, amongst acres of moorland and silver sheets of sunset-reflecting water is fuel to my soul.

I've always stayed later than I intended, always dragged the day out into the night. A few more casts, a last pipe-full, a last coffee or a wee dram to keep out the cold; I've always found it difficult to leave. This summer it's been almost impossible. The cottage can sometimes seem cold now, despite the crackle of flames from the log burner. Sometimes it can feel a little unwelcoming, just a little. And it sounds different. Everyday noises are louder somehow; the whole place seems to echo at the slightest opportunity as if I've stripped the place of furniture, despite having altered not a single thing. It sounds empty and really, it is empty; at least partially so, anyway. Half of its soul has been removed.

While I had my fish, Mary had her sea eagles. They were her passion, an antidote to the constant loss she felt and a distraction to the subliminal questions that seeped from her family.

In a place where family is everything, an absence of children can be unthinkable. While parents, aunts, uncles and cousins hid their confusion at our lack of offspring, we kept on trying and kept on failing. And, as we got to an age where we realised it wasn't going to happen and gave up, she found her eagles. She watched and she cared for them as if they were her surrogate children, throwing herself into 'motherhood' with a fervour that overrode everything else in her life. Campaigns, interviews with the local media, school visits and lectures, all to raise awareness, keep her eagles safe and to let them raise a chick or two each year.

Each springtime, everything else in her life became secondary for her. I didn't mind too much; spring is a good time to be out with a fly rod after all, but nature can be a cruel mistress and some years her pain seemed immense. The first few years, her eagles struggled. Like us, they too seemed desperate to raise a family but also like us, didn't seem very good at it. Even when they'd sorted everything out and got the whole mating and nesting routine working like clockwork, a cold spell with strong north winds at the wrong time meant an abandoned nest and disaster for the chicks. Heavy rain another year caused the ground to flood and a waterfall to pour down the cliff face; nest and eggs washed into the sea. At each failing Mary would be inconsolable for a week or a month and I would keep quiet and let her come back to me.

We had lost two of our own after all.

But most years, her eagles did their thing and nature played along. She would then, at some time in June, be impossible for a week or more, barely eating, hardly sleeping, constantly at the bottom of our croft, in her hide, watching, waiting for the chicks to fledge. She was like a teenager again, overflowing with energy and determination. And most years, when, amidst much flapping and hopping, the youngsters took their first leap of faith, I was there with her, holding her hand and sharing her joy.

You died on a Tuesday in May, in bed, while you slept. Actually while we slept. And I didn't realise. I didn't know. To all intents and purposes, I wasn't even there; I was in the land of dreams while you took a long slow breath and let it out for the last time. I have but one regret in my life; that I wasn't able to hold your hand and kiss your warm lips one last time.

That year, the year you died, your eagles reared a pair of chicks. There were no casualties, no real difficulties, good weather, good feeding and good fortune. They were lucky. I think they had your portion of luck that year. Perhaps, as you died, you gave them your last reserves of will, and that kept them safe.

I watched her, your eagle, rise from the cliff top the day the chicks flew the nest. She soared, vertically through warm June air with a sense of freedom that I felt in my gut, before diving and swooping, twisting her wings and somersaulting over and over. I swear she was simply happy to be alive and flew in a celebration of her existence and in elation for the success of her offspring.

I watched for a tumultuous hour, thinking of you and how you would have wept with joy. Overlooking that cliff top, the pain of losing you still heavy within me, it was as if she was celebrating your life as well as her own. Tears dried on my cheeks, leaving salty tracks.

I always thought that, if I were left on my own, I'd probably sell up and move back to the mainland, that I'd rekindle my relationship with the city. I always thought that I'd feel lost without you and, though the emptiness of the cottage is often difficult, it seems the island and your eagles aren't quite finished with me after all.

The snipe still thrums and the fence post at my back still holds some of the day's warmth. Like Mary's eagle, I too ought to be making my way home. But I have some coffee left and a small dram to make it taste even better, my pipe is still glowing and the landscape around me is relaxing, exhaling the day's last breath as night approaches.

I'll stay a little while longer yet.

22. Na h-Iolairean
by Suzanne Arnold

Bha e faisg air bliadhna a-nis o chaochail an duine aice
ach bha i fhathast a' faireachdainn leth-mharbh i fhèin.
Bha an t-uisge a' taomadh a-nuas timcheall air a' chàr
agus cha mhòr gum faiceadh i càil sam bith tron uinneig.
Bha i coma. Chaidh i ann air sgàth 's gun robh i a'
smaoineachadh gun lorgadh i sìth ann. Ach cha do lorg.
Cha robh i a' lorg fois ann an àite sam bith. Dh'fhàg i am
baile mòr seach gun robh a h-uile caraid ro choibhneil.
Cha robh iad ag iarraidh a fàgail na h-aonar. Cha robh ise
airson a bhith còmhla ri duine sam bith. Mura biodh
Robbie ann, b' fhèarr leatha a bhith na h-aonar. Bha i air
an taigh aice ann an Sasainn a reic agus air seann taigh a
cheannach faisg air a' mhuir air eilean beag Albannach.
Dìreach nuair a bha i a' dol a thilleadh dhachaigh, chuir i
na *wipers* air, agus chunnaic i eun mòr air iteig thar a'
chuain. Ghabh Màiri greim air a' phrosbaig ach bha i ro
fhadalach. Chaidh an t-eun seachad ro luath agus chaidh
e à sealladh air cùl na beinne.

B' e seo a' chiad uair a bha ùidh aig Màiri ann an càil
sam bith. Gu ruige seo, chan fhaiceadh i carson a bhiodh
dad inntinneach dhi mura biodh Robbie a' gabhail pàirt
ann cuideachd. Dh'fhuirich i anns a' chàr fad leth-uair

eile, a' coimhead a-mach air an uinneig ach chan fhaca i ach uisge a' fàs na bu truime 's na bu truime.

Thill i dhachaigh, rinn i cupan tì agus smaoinich i mu dheidhinn an eòin mhòir. Bha i cinnteach gur e iolaire a bh' ann. Chan fhaca i iolaire a-riamh ach bha fios aice gun robh iad air an eilean seo. Thug i na leabhraichean a-mach bhon a' phreas. Cha robh ùidh mhòr aice ann an eun-eòlais ach bha Robbie làn eòlais air a h-uile rud nàdarrach, gu sònraichte na h-eòin. Rinn i snodha-gàire beag nuair a chunnaic i an àireamh de leabhraichean a bh' ann. Bha iad brèagha. Bha Robbie air a dhòigh nuair a bha e air eun ùr fhaicinn agus air a rannsachadh anns na leabhraichean aige. Choimhead i air na leabhraichean agus smaoinich Màiri cho mìorbhalach 's a bhiodh e iolaire fhaicinn na b' fhaisge.

Bu toil le Màiri peantadh agus nuair a chaidh i fhèin is Robbie air saor-làithean, mar a b' àbhaist, bhiodh iad a' draibheadh gu tuath agus a' fuireach ann an taigh samhraidh airson seachdain no dhà. Bu toil leotha àiteachan gu math iomallach agus bhiodh Robbie a' coimhead air na h-eòin fhad 's a bhiodh ise a' dèanamh sgeidseachan ann an leabhar beag agus a' togail dhealbhan le camara. Bhon a' chiad turas a chaidh iad dhan Ghàidhealtachd, b' e bòidhchead nam beann an cuspair a bha i ag iarraidh sna dealbhan aice. Bha atharrachaidhean an t-solais a' còrdadh rithe gu mòr. Bha i toilichte a' peantadh an aon sealladh grunn thursan air sàillibh 's gum biodh e a' coimhead eadar-dhealaichte gach turas a rèir àm an latha, àm na bliadhna agus gu dearbh, na h-aimsire. Bha gaol aig Màiri air an dùthaich, a bhith a' peantadh a-muigh, ach cha robh e cho furasta anns an àite seo far an robh an t-sìde fliuch gu math tric. Co-dhiù, uaireannan, thogadh i dealbhan beaga le camara agus an uair sin, air ais san taigh, pheantadh i dealbhan mòra brèagha dhe na ghlac i.

An ath-sheachdain, chaidh Màiri air ais dhan àite far am faca i an t-eun mòr oir cha b' urrainn dhi a dhìochuimhneachadh. Bha an t-sìde na b' fheàrr an turas seo agus streap i gu mullach cnuic. Dh'fhuirich i ann fad an fheasgair ach chan fhaca i ach faoileagan, feannagan glasa agus eòin bheaga eile. Bha briseadh dùil oirre ach air an t-slighe dhachaigh, ruith còig fèidh tarsainn air an rathad. Stad i an càr agus lean i iad le a sùilean gus an deach iad a-mach à sealladh. "Tha an-còmhnaidh rudeigin an seo a chuireas iongnadh orm," thuirt i rithe fhèin.

Chùm Màiri oirre a' tilleadh a-rithist is a-rithist chun an àite ud far am faca i an t-eun mòr. Bha an geamhradh a' tighinn a-nis ach bha aodach blàth aig Màiri. Ged a bha an t-uisge a' dòrtadh sìos ghabh i a-mach às a' chàr agus thòisich i a' streap na creige. Cha robh i ach letheach slighe suas nuair a chunnaic i e. An turas seo, cha robh e cho fada air falbh bhuaipe. Cha do leig i h-anail.

Cho mòr is cumhachdach, dh'itealaich e gu h-àrd gus an robh e os cionn Màiri. Chaidh e mun cuairt aon turas agus an uair sin, chunnaic i eun eile ri thaobh. Dìreach an uair sin, thàinig a' ghrian a-mach às na sgòthan agus chunnaic i cho buidhe 's a bha a cheann – fiù 's òr-bhuidhe. Chaidh iad timcheall is timcheall fad deich mionaidean agus lean Màiri le sùilean iad gus an do chaill i thar mullach na beinne iad.

Tron gheamhradh, thill i air ais gu math tric agus chunnaic i an dà iolaire bho àm gu àm. Dh'fheuch i ri dealbhan a thogail dhiubh le camara ach cha b' urrainn dhi an dealbh a bha i ag iarraidh fhaighinn. Aig an taigh bha i a' peantadh dealbh mòr dhen tìr agus bha i ag iarraidh iolaire a chur ann, ach cha robh i airson a dhèanamh gun a bhith ceart. Rinn i tòrr lethbhreacan de dh'iolairean bho na leabhraichean aig Robbie ach cha robh i buileach toilichte leotha. Cha robh iàd a' coimhead beòthail gu leòr.

An ath thuras, streap i a' bheinn a-rithist agus shuidh i fo chraoibh faisg air a' mhullach. An dèidh greis thòisich i a' dèanamh dealbh peansail dhe na craobhan air a' bheinn. Bha an t-àite cho ciùin, bha i a' faireachdainn gu math socair mar gun robh spiorad Robbie ri a taobh. Nach biodh esan toilichte gun robh ùidh aig Màiri anns na h-iolairean a-nis. Nuair a bha i a' smaoineachadh mu dheidhinn seo, chuala i fuaim beag os a cionn, agus chunnaic i an dà iolaire a' dol dhan chraoibh gu math faisg oirre.

Choimhead i orra is iad a' gluasad tro mheangan na craoibhe agus, gan leantainn le sùilean. Chunnaic i gun robh tòrr fhaillean aig cùl na craoibhe, air an cruinneachadh eadar meangan mòr agus oir na creige. "An e nead a tha siud?" smaoinich i.

"A bheil thu a' faicinn a' nead?" thuirt guth ìosal air a cùlaibh.

Thionndaidh i agus chunnaic i fear dubh feusagach na shuidhe air a cùlaibh. "Gabh mo leisgeul", ars esan, "cha robh mi ag iarraidh eagal a chur ort ach chunnaic mi thu a' tighinn an seo agus cha robh mi cinnteach an robh fios agad mu dheidhinn a' nead. Tha mi fhìn a' fuireach anns a' ghleann agus tha mi a' cumail sùil air. Gu mì-fhortanach, chan eil a h-uile duine a' tighinn airson dealbhan a thogail".

Thionndaidh Màiri air ais chun an nid agus, gu h-iongantach, bha na h-iolairean an sin fhathast. "Seall, tha na h-iolairean dol a' sgèith a-nis." ars an duine. Ghabh i greim air a' chamara agus, *cliog, cliog, cliog,* fhuair i na dealbhan a bha i ag iarraidh mu dheireadh thall: dà iolaire a' sgèith còmhla ri chèile.

"Tha e a' fàs fuar." thuirt an duine. "A bheil thu ag iarraidh tighinn air ais airson cupan tì?"

"Nach dèan mi sin?" fhreagair i.

the skies

23. Lewisian Nights
by Garry MacKenzie

Abandoned air force buildings – mess hall,
dormitories, clifftop cells where visions
of war were drawn from a metal sea –

have become a village, concrete shells
that sheep wander like tinkers. In the cold war
of wind and land, two crofts remain,

and pillboxes black with peat
guard a beach whose sand
was sucked into the sea.

Cows stand in the rain. Inside we drink
and talk of ferry crossings, first impressions,
sitting in a crofthouse kitchen

built for radar operators' wives.
At each pause in conversation
we contemplate the inner exile.

Later, our hostess lifts a gun
and none of us is shocked or laughs
as feathers fall near the cattle trough:

a gull flies west with the sun, lead-poisoned.
Night sweeps its ash into the sky.
A bus rattles at the end of the road.

24. Latha Math airson Cuairt
by Catrìona Lexy Chaimbeul

Uisge fodhainn,
uisge m' ar coinneamh,
uisge a' dòrtadh,
is uisge gar cuairteachadh.

Tha an Cuan Siar a' deàrrsadh nad shùilean
a tha den aon dath –
gorm-ghlas.

Tro ghleadhraich na gèile is briseadh nan tonn,
tha mi gad chluinntinn
ag èigheachd le sunnd:
"Latha math airson cuairt".

24. A Fine Day for a Walk
by Catriona Lexy Chaimbeul

Water beneath us,
water before us,
rain pouring
and water surrounding us.

The Atlantic shines in your eyes
that are the same colour –
blue-grey.

Through the roar of the wind and the breaking of
waves,
I hear you
shouting joyously:
"A fine day for a walk".

25. **Rionnagan**
by Catrìona Lexy Chaimbeul

Cha mhòr nach robh mi air
dìochuimhneachadh
gun robh leithid a' rud ann
ri rionnagan.
Mìltean de ghathan beaga geal
san dorchadas.
An t-sìorraidheachd a' cadal
bhos mo cheann.
Fiù 's le mo fhradharc cumhang
chì mi fhathast gach nì
a bha
agus a bhios
is nach robh 's nach bi.
Ann an dubh na h-oidhche,
fo fharsaingeachd gun chrìch,
tha mi a' gabhail sòlas
ann an neonitheachd.

25. Stars
by Catrìona Lexy Chaimbeul

I had almost
forgotten
there was such a thing
as stars.
Thousands of tiny, white stabs
in the dark.
Eternity sleeps
above my head.
Even with my narrow sight
I can still see everything
that was
and that will be
and was not and won't be.
In the black of the night,
beneath an endless expanse,
I take comfort
in nothingness.

26. Flood
by Susie Southall

It was relentless.
Fields, featureless and dull, one day shone, saturated.

Next morning the mud,
Oozing and inching, cold brown lava in waves from
the flat top hill.

It came, smell first and silently.
Crept into gardens and ponds, carried sacrifices down
in the camber.

People looked on helpless.
Watched it seep under doors, swallow carpets, ease
between tiles.

And we three, eyes wide and jaws dropped
Stood on our corner aghast.
Wonder turning to unruly teenage joy
As we danced our thanks, shin deep in liquid soil
And whooping under a clearing sky.

people

27. Before the Bridge was Built
by Alison Lang

Before the bridge was built, no priest had ever set foot on the island. No minister either, in case you thought denomination made a difference. No, in those days the islanders had no truck with disseminators of the gospel, and no interest in the politics that divided them one sect from another in the law courts and universities of the mainland.

There were those in the capital who would, from time to time, in what little respite they found from publishing their tracts and arguing over doctrinal minutiae, dream up schemes to civilise the people of the islands. And to some extent the earnest young missionaries they sent forth were succeeding, because there were certain islands where great spiritual harvests had been reaped even from the stoniest ground, thanks to their zeal for reform and the tireless fundraising of the charitable ladies who organised temperance teas and concerts of faith-affirming music.

But such miracles were possible only if an island could be reached and traversed in safety, and that required co-operation. It required help to land at the quayside, where there was a quayside, or to haul a boat up a stony beach and secure it above the tide line. It required the availability of food and lodgings, of horses or mules and of accurate directions to the next township. And there were tales of men of God who had mistaken their path, fallen from cliffs, drowned in ditches or simply disappeared without trace.

As if the territory alone did not present challenge enough, the missionaries had found the people suspicious, slow to respond, some of them deliberately unhelpful. Gradually, though – thanks to God's grace, you may say – their resistance weakened and the great work of evangelism began to bear fruit. On some islands, at least. But not on this one.

Without the bridge, there were two ways to cross to the island, by boat or by wading across the ford, which was passable only at certain times of day and on some days not at all. The thin-faced priest had assumed it would be easy to find a boat, but rumours of his mission had gone before him and the fishermen seemed deaf to his hailing and hollering from the shore. As they made their way to and fro along the narrow channel, their backs turned steadfastly towards him, they sailed so close that he could clearly see the patterns on their jerseys, but they continued to ignore him.

What childish behaviour these fishermen exhibited, taunting him in this way. But they were like children, he reminded himself, and it was his duty to teach them how to put aside childish things. If only he could reach the island.

From the stretch of shore where he stood waving in vain at the boats, it was an hour's journey to the ford. Had he known about it, he could have followed the well-worn track that lay a little distance inland, but as it was he forged his own path through prickly bushes and jagged rocks along the water's edge. The fishermen must have seen him, and they must have laughed, but he persevered. "Strait is the gate," he reminded himself, "and narrow is the way, which leadeth unto life, and few there be that find it."

He hoped he would not have to wade too deep, because he had brought with him a large number of instructional books and pamphlets, printed in the capital at considerable expense, and he was reluctant to get them wet. Had he known that no one on the island could read, he might have jettisoned these items and tried, despite his lack of skill and ignorance of the currents, to swim across the fishermen's thoroughfare. But he still had much to learn about the islanders.

The sun was high when at last he reached the ford, and the priest was sweating and dishevelled, his feet were wet and he had dropped his baggage more than once. This was clearly the place. On the other side of the water he could see houses and a track leading up the hill. Ruts made by cartwheels showed that it must be possible to drive a wagon across and that several must have gone this way recently, but he could see no other signs of life.

Gingerly he stepped into the water, gathering his belongings about him and trying to keep the precious books at shoulder height. Three paces brought the water to his knees, two more to his thighs and another to his waist. He felt the tug of the current on his coat tails. Suddenly the silt beneath his feet felt soft, sucking at his boots. Knowing that haste or panic could be his undoing, he summoned his strength and stepped as steadily as he could backwards, one step at a time. His wet clothes weighed him down as he retreated to safety, clinging to his legs and causing him to shiver despite the heat of the day.

As he sat on the shore, he thought of how our Lord had walked on water. He remembered too that it was the fisherman who had first heeded the call to follow Him. And how could a humble priest, frail and fearful as he was, persuade the fishermen and the other island folk to follow him if he couldn't even reach them? The island seemed so near. The houses opposite mocked him with their proximity. He closed his eyes in prayer, and it was when he opened them that he first set eyes on Annag.

In later years, when the bridge building had begun, Annag would remember her first encounter with the thin-faced priest, how she saw him sitting there on the ground on the mainland side of the water, dripping wet and muttering into his clasped hands. Such a little man, hardly bigger than a child, and so thin you could have snapped his arms and legs off.

The islanders were stoutly built people. Were and are, as you'll see if you look around you today. Annag herself stood well over six foot tall. Strength was more to be prized than grace or elegance among the women, for it was they who would carry the men folk out to their boats, so as to keep their feet dry. It would not do to begin a day's fishing with wet feet, after all, and the women could return to the shore and get themselves dry again.

Yes, they were used to wading and carrying, and that was how Annag came to work the ford. The terrible storm that sunk her husband's boat also changed the contours of the island, tearing down a jetty, swallowing up a whole headland and deepening the channel that had always been easy to wade across. There were not many tall enough to cross it after that, but a widow must find a way to make a living.

In other parts of the country – more civilised and godly places, you might say – it would have been considered unseemly for a woman to carry a man on her back or shoulders, but the islanders were pragmatic and had not yet been taught to feel shame. And for Annag, who was famous for her love of gossip, the job gave her the additional advantage of knowing before anyone else what manner of people might be coming to the island, what business they had there, the duration of their stay and more about their physique, clothing and personal hygiene than might be deemed decent for ladies of gentler breeding.

The tide was still low, so at its deepest the water reached only to Annag's thighs. Hoisting her skirts and knotting them about her loins like a great nappy, she waded into the channel and strode towards the priest who sat transfixed, not simply by the approach of such a monstrous Amazon but by the horror of seeing her naked legs. Never had he witnessed such a spectacle of immodesty. She may not have meant to excite or entice, but he couldn't tear his eyes away.

He had heard of the women of ill repute to whom some of his colleagues felt it their mission to minister in the worst districts of the cities, particularly the ports, and he wondered for a moment whether it was proximity to water that impelled women to disrobe in such an indecent fashion. But Annag's display of abundant flesh, rosy and glistening now as she splashed nearer and nearer, wasn't intentionally wanton or seductive. It was simply a practical solution to the problem of drying off all those heavy flannel petticoats, by not getting them wet in the first place.

Annag loomed over the thin-faced priest, extending her hand to help him up. Standing at full height, he was at eye level with her bosom.

"It's a penny to cross," she told him.

The poor man hardly knew where to look, straight ahead at her breasts, down at her legs or up into the face that seemed too far above him to allow a normal exchange of polite glances. Already he felt his encounter with this woman was too intimate for comfort, and now his only option was to cling to her body, to wrap his legs around that broad waist and his arms about those shoulders. He shivered with fear and with other sensations he had often felt before and just as often sought to suppress. He thought of turning back, but he knew he had to go on.

He fished in his pocket for a penny and held it out to her, hesitantly, like a naughty child expecting punishment. Taking the penny, Annag tucked it into the depths of her bosom in full view of the priest, who averted his eyes in shame only to focus next on her bulging knees. He turned instead to collect his bags, and no sooner had he lifted them than he found himself snatched up into the air and flung into a piggyback hold so tight that he gasped and squealed.

What he wanted to think about was St Christopher, who had carried the Christ child across a river. What he wanted to remember was that as the child grew more and more heavy on his shoulders, weighed down by the sins of the world, the humble saint had recognised his passenger's true identity. What he actually thought about was the warmth of Annag's back and the wetness of his trousers against it. In moments like these, prayer was undoubtedly the appropriate refuge from temptation. Temptation? He hardly liked to acknowledge that this was what he felt.

Annag didn't speak again until they were half way across. She found that people would reveal more if questioned at the right moment, especially if they feared that failure to divulge their business might land them in the water.

And when she asked him his reason for coming to the island, he couldn't help but tell her that it was to save her soul. And when she asked why he should want to save her soul, he couldn't help but tell her that it was because he was bidden by God to love her.

Annag stopped in her tracks. She was not unused to declarations of love and had received several before her marriage and many since her husband's death, but the men who made them had been motivated by the prospect of getting a useful wife who could work hard, lift peats, mend the roof and wade out to their fishing boats. This man, this helpless little man with his thin face and his wet clothes and his pointless books, had never seen her before and surely did not seek from her what the island men had sought, so what was she to make of his extraordinary claim?

When they reached the island, the priest clung to Annag and she made no move to set him down, and for what seemed an eternity – but may have been only a few moments – she stood on the shore, her skirts tucked up indecently high, feeling on the back of her neck the fluttering breath of the strange man who said he loved her.

The little man hung there, light-headed, his thoughts in turmoil. He prayed – no, he hoped – that she would not set him down, not yet, for his legs felt so weak that he feared they would not support him if he tried to stand. Something had happened on the way across the ford. Something had changed irrevocably. And suddenly he knew that the moment his feet touched the ground he would no longer be the same man who had set out for the island.

After the bridge was built, other priests would come to the island. And not only priests, but ministers and missionaries and catechists and schoolmasters and government inspectors. The earliest of these visitors may have known about the mission of the thin-faced priest and wondered whatever befell him. But if anyone knew the comings and goings of the island it was Annag, and in all her lore and stories she never admitted to knowing of a priest gone a-missing.

And later, once the island was officially considered civilised, no one would remember the thin-faced priest or his failure to evangelise the fishermen and their stalwart women, and gradually memories would fade of how remote and alien such places had once seemed.

The islanders have always been stoutly built people, as you can see if you look about you even today, and they say that Annag's daughters favoured her in that respect. Strength was always more to be prized than delicacy among the islanders, even if they would never again need to wade across the ford.

28. The School of the Seven Bells
by Bob Jenkins

Their friendship was born on a dreadful, dreich day. One of those smirr-filled days. The cold crept through the soles of Aeneas's boots and the damp ate through his coat until it bit deep into his sinewy muscles but he stoically continued with his repairs of the sea-wall.

The sea-wall on Rua had been built many centuries before, not to protect the land from the sea but to protect the land from the Islanders' sheep. Rua sheep lived on the seaward side of the wall, surviving on seaweed whilst the precious grazing inside the wall was reserved for the Islanders' cattle and a few potatoes. As the island's population shrunk the task of repairs had come to rest entirely upon Aeneas's shoulders and he was faced with this urgent repair, following a major fall, on, of all days, a Sunday.

Aeneas was cooried down rebuilding the foundations of the dry-stane dyke when a face appeared above his head. The contrast with Aeneas could not have been more dramatic. Aeneas was so weather-beaten that his features could have been hewn from a solid block of mahogany. The new face was silhouetted against a bible black sky and looked vulnerable, almost transparent. The skin was as translucent as a baby's fontanelle and the features were weak and frail, as though about to be blown apart like a storm-struck hayrick.

"Peace be upon you."

Aeneas looked up and nodded. "A fine day for it."

"Indeed. I thought that I would have the island to myself today. I assumed everybody would be in church."

"God forfend. You won't find me in the kirk. I'm the black sheep of the island, living with the devil in my head according to the minister. As far as he's concerned when I left the Church of Scotland I converted to paganism."

"And did you?"

Aeneas paused for a moment then, in his delicate, almost soporific island accent said "perhaps, I like to think that I'm spiritual not religious. The past and the present are always here with us on Rua. Some of our ways are as old as these hills and go back to times long before the hermit monks brought Christianity hereabouts. I try to follow those ways."

Aeneas had stood up and stretched his back whilst he spoke. He held a rock in each hand and appeared to be weighing them rather than visualising their suitability for the next level of the dyke.

"What happened?" asked the stranger, nodding at the pile of rock that had once been a wall.

"Ach rabbits undercut the dyke and it tumbled in the storm. I'll have it fixed in no time. Fortunately the sheep were weathering the storm over on the other side" and he pointed across the island. "I'll need to repair it before they discover the gap."

"When do you bring the sheep inside the wall? I've never discovered a gate."

Aeneas laughed again. "The sheep stay outside the wall for their whole life. Well, until they're ready for market that is." Aeneas had placed the stranger. He was the monk from the Big House.

"And they survive on seaweed?"

"Indeed. These old sheep have survived on seaweed for hundreds of generations and the outside world is so intrigued by them that they pay me a premium for them. People pay an awful lot of money for a Rua chop."

"Do they taste different?"

"I can't say if they do. It's all I've ever been used to but it's not my place to question that demand. I simply accept the bounty. Try some yourself and tell me."

"I'm afraid I shall have to forego that pleasure. We are vegetarians at the Temple." They stood silently together for a moment. "Well, I'll leave you to your work. It looks as though you have plenty to do."

"Ach, I'll soon have the dyke redd up again. It'll be good as new before the sheep ken it was down."

"Pity about the weather."

"I'm alright. I might have taken my first steps into dotage but I quite like the sound of rain when I'm alone, it's like silence but not empty. I'm content here, alone with my thoughts."

"Bless you. Maybe I'll return to talk to you soon. One of my lessons taught me that a single conversation with a wise man is worth ten years of study. You have given me much to consider," and the monk bowed and left Aeneas alone on the beach.

Aeneas watched the tiny figure shuffle away, half expecting a gust to fill the little man's puffer jacket and lift him from the ground and blow him out to sea.

Slowly, over the following weeks, a wary friendship developed. The monk would set out on walks around Rua until he found Aeneas at some task. Aeneas, with his Angus Og brogue and his Islanders' insatiable curiosity, questioned the monk on the purpose of their temple and the reasons for so many young people arriving on the ferry and disappearing into the Big House. The monk's explanations did not really make sense to Aeneas. Personal crisis and relationship breakdown were, Aeneas considered, part of everybody's experience and to be dealt with quietly and personally by those involved, not by a wider community.

The monk questioned Aeneas about island life and the island itself. Aeneas regularly found himself abandoning the task in hand and leading the monk across the machair to illustrate some aspect of geology or botany or animal husbandry. He explained how the prevailing wind blew from the west so the few westerly buildings were largely tucked in folds which protected them from the Atlantic. The eastern edge of Rua was more benign, facing the Sea of the Hebrides, and more populated and there a harbour had been constructed. 'Moods change here with the moon, the wind, the currents.'

Each time they met the monk took some knowledge away and, in turn, Aeneas became more interested in the ceremonies underlying the monk's beliefs and, in particular, in the paraphernalia of his religion. The monk explained the purpose of the prayer flags and temple chimes. He said that they had a series of temples inside the Big House, now called the 'School of the Seven Bells,' and he invited Aeneas to visit but Aeneas politely turned down the invitation. "That would be the final straw in my eternal damnation, according to the minister and his faithful flock, entering a Buddhist temple."

On one of those perfect, glorious days, when the seas sparkled and the machair glittered with an endless bouquet of wild flowers, Aeneas was repairing a fence when the monk appeared silently at his side.

"The sky is so blue it would make you believe in angels."

The monk laughed like the chuckling of water. "I thought that you had abandoned Christianity."

Aeneas considered, then said, "No, I'm not sure. Sometimes I watch the seas flow beyond the sunset and I just marvel at the beauty and I want to give thanks, to praise God for the splendour which surrounds me. Look at the carpet he has provided for us. Every single bloom is a miniature gem. I find myself taking more and more joy from such beauty. I find grace in tiny things that previously I ignored. I find it hard to believe that there is some cosmic lord of the dance who controls the emotions and events of the universe but surely all of this beauty did not happen by chance."

"Where else would you rather be but Rua? Here's a quote for you. 'In a wickedly hostile universe Scotland is a sweet place to be.' That's from a great, modern day philosopher called Kris Kristofferson."

The monk chuckled again. "The singer?"

"Indeed. A clever man, with a love for Scotland. Life can be hard here. This is no climate for a sane person to live in, which might explain an awful lot, but it is home, my home, and I love it dearly. I might not be wired up right but I am content here. I'm making my journey, learning much along the way. Life has not yielded up all of its secrets to me, but it will."

"We have a saying that gems cannot be polished without friction, nor a man without trials."

"There's truth in that but I think we probably suffer more trials on Rua than most. Does that polish us more?"

"I'm not sure if there's a direct relationship. Do you think people on the island are more spiritually aware?"

"To be honest, no. I think the 'thou shalt not' dictates of the Presbyterian kirk brutally kick out any spirituality. My dear wife attended every service, every bible group, every meeting. She was sweet as a rose but prickly as a thistle and she would claim total faith, total belief, in her God but that faith came by rote, from the sermons she obediently absorbed, not love."

"Do you miss her?" They were leaning against a cattle fank.

"When she died the wind spilled out of my sails", Aeneas said sadly with his slow-paced, musical cadence. "May the angels guard her sleep."

Seagulls ack-acked machine gun rattles over their heads and disturbed their tranquillity so they began to stroll, blethering away, heads close together.

Their friendship developed further over that year. The seasons passed. Storms raged, tides rose and the community went about its routines. Days shortened and their walks shortened too until, more regularly, their conversations took place in Aeneas's little cottage. He had offered the monk a dram on his first visit, as island hospitality demanded, but it was politely refused and they developed their own tea ceremony most afternoons. 'Ceremony is the smoke of friendship' the monk had claimed and Aeneas had responded with "I've never got the hang of tea bags. I'll just serve it in the old way, you'll understand."

Christmas arrived. At one time, not so long before, you would never have spotted decorated Christmas trees or fairy-lights on Rua but times had changed and a few houses even strung lights along their eaves, a brave and rash action given the regularity of hurricane-strength gales thereabouts. Aeneas himself had strung up some tinsel in his living room to create a little bit of seasonal joy.

The monk rattled the door, let himself in, and then bowed and presented a parcel to Aeneas. Aeneas was embarrassed. He valued his friendship with the monk, and had been generous to his other friends, but he had decided that it would be inappropriate to give the monk a Christmas gift. He was not a Christian so surely did not celebrate Christmas.

"What is it?"

"Open the parcel and receive enlightenment" the monk giggled.

Inside was a palm-sized, leather bound book. 'Refuge: Finding a Purpose and a Path' by Lama Dilgo Rinpoche.

"That's you, Dilgo. You never told me you had written a book."

"It's just published. I had started writing it when we established our temple here but I was struggling to find the words that I needed, struggling to explain personal enlightenment satisfactorily. I was blocked, seeking inspiration in the natural world, when I met you that day down at the sea-wall and then we talked and my writer's block cleared. Look at the dedication."

Aeneas turned the pages until he found the dedication. 'To my friend Aeneas Mackinnon, at whose feet I have studied and received enlightenment.'

"You have taught me much, Aeneas. I spent my childhood in Sikkim, studying with Lamas of all four Tibetan orders and then I was sent out to spread our teachings and to provide illumination to those who struggle with the world. I believed that life on Rua would be such a dramatic change that, like the early Christian monks, pilgrims would surely find some inner peace and solace if they dedicated time to their spiritual studies here. We bought our temple and moved in but we were different, apart from the Islanders. You helped me immeasurably. You radiate a joy and understand your world. You focus ancient energies, ancient knowledge, and you shared all of that with me. I have used the lessons you taught me about island traditions and nurturing your bounties to share with our pilgrims and I believe that your teachings will affect them for all of their lives. Your teachings have already opened their eyes and it is your wisdom that forms the foundations of my book. You are my guru Aeneas."

Aeneas was stunned. The worst characteristic that any Islander can display is an overblown sense of importance and here was a whole book that the monk was claiming was based on his 'insights and illuminations.' Aeneas's heart sank.

"I have a request, Aeneas. Please come with me and visit our temple for the first time. Please permit me to introduce you to my pilgrims. They have heard so much of your wisdom and each has spent hours considering the meanings of your teachings."

Aeneas was startled into a response. "No way, Dilgo, never. You've misled me. No. It's wrong."

"Sorry, Aeneas. I'll go, I am truly sorry if I have upset you but please read the book" and the monk backed out of the door.

Aeneas reluctantly settled down in his winged armchair and placed more peat on the fire and began to read. He felt indulgent yet unwillingly smiled at some of his own phrases which Dilgo had recorded. He poured himself a glass of whisky and smiled at the lessons Dilgo had taken from Aeneas's 'putting up' driftwood above the high water line and his cutting peats over the summer. He burst out laughing at the way his views about what should and what should not be reported to the Official Receiver of Wrecks was recorded.

Aeneas read into the night until he completed the book. Dilgo had faithfully recorded many of Aeneas's thoughts and then provided insights that Aeneas himself could never have found the words to express. Aeneas sat on, staring into the dark and trying to decide if he had been used or if the book held any value. All he could really complain about was that Dilgo had not warned him that his thoughts were being recorded

Dawn broke and Aeneas set off towards the Big House. He would never be able to call it the 'Bodhicharya School of Seven Bells' but as he approached the front door he was stopped by the sight of seven ornate cylinders fixed in a row in a wall. Aeneas felt compelled to run his hands across their surfaces as he passed and, in turn, each cylinder spun to clang musically and send music tinkling out across Rua on the westerly winds.

The front door of the house was thrown open and a voice welcomed Aeneas with "Remove your shoes and leave the dust of the world outside. Please enter." Aeneas did as he was bid and entered the temple.

29. Cànan nan Gàidheal
by Morag Henriksen

Why can I not speak Gaelic,
my father's mother's tongue,
when folk around me had it?

My mother never spoke it
although she understood
more than she would admit.
I did not care to build a barrier
between my Mum and me.

"Tha an cat glas. Bha an gad cam."
I learned my primer just to please my father
but English was the patois of the playground
and Gaelic, timetabled with Art,
just didn't stand a chance.

But most of all
it bored me stiff
to sit in church and count the *agus*es
while Gaelic roared and rumbled overhead
and made me feel my guilt.
For Gaelic was the language of the church,
the language of repression.

Tha an cat glas : The cat is grey.   *Agus:*   and
Bha an gad cam: The twig is crooked

30. Lexie Moffat Screams
by Linda Henderson

Her Grannie McIlroy's voice.

    -      Lexie Moffat was born in a cow shed.

Her Auntie Senna.

    -      Not so.

    -      Do not believe the first thing you are told by that witch of a sister of mine. You were a wee blot of a thing. I saw your mother carry you up to the house and it was definitely the pig yard she was headed from. Blood streaming down her legs, you wrapped in a shred of butter muslin.

The silver birches, tall and straight mostly, and hung with lichen. Pegged-out washing. Soft mounds of moss, kicking ant nests, very blue skies, washing in the loch. Icy.

Women squabbling. Women, and having filthy hands. No men, no touch of a man's hand. No whiskers about her face - much later on.

A tomb of Caithness slabs, wrought iron railings among unmarked mounds, up the hill. Running her fingers over the encrusted inscription, her Granny there to visit Gramps. Not knowing any of the letters. Granny's voice.

-      A daughter of Moy, young and beautiful, she was. She died on her wedding night. Some said she was already wasting; others say it was Jack Fraser's doing. He took her just the once and smothered her with his thanks.

Lexie's father. Did she know him? Can she kick-start that conversation so long ago before he was forgotten along with almost everything else Lexie once knew that she knew.

Senna's voice.

-      Jamie Milk, Norrie MacWhinney?

Granny's voice.

-      That's not his real name, Senna. He wasn't Norrie at all. He was....

-      The Macrae boys?

-      More likely that father of theirs or even the old man himself. They say he could never get enough.

-      You should know, Christina Beaton McIlroy. You should know.

The name, Christina, comes out of nowhere into Lexie's mind. She doesn't think she ever heard it used again. Granny's voice.

- That Allan Drew's yer man.
- Aye. Just so, though how she must have wheedled and coaxed him into any of the outhouses is beyond me. Let alone have got him to, you know.

Lexie Moffat can't remember the words for that thing. A man's thing. Lexie Moffat screams.

**

The windows of the nursing home look down the Loch to the south east. A ridge of mountains on the mainland curtains the horizon but Lexie in her wheelchair parked up as close as they can get her does not lift her eyes to the hills but scans the water. Always looking for birds. Four grey lag geese slide into land, their feet forward, skimming hard and deep, braking, folding their wings. Close into the shore.

Drawing her name. Counting aloud. Some days at the village school. Senna's voice.

- That girl should go more often. She might make more of herself.

Her mother's voice. A rare intrusion.

-   I need her here. We need her here.

She knows she could draw the letters of her own name. Put a pencil stub in her fingers now. She is Alexandra Beaton McIlroy. Her tongue is working the shapes of the letters. She fills a whole sheet of paper. She says the alphabet in her head.

**

Cathy's voice.
-   A nice cup of tea, Mrs Moffat? Can I get you tea? A biscuit perhaps. We have a bourbon or a nice Nice today. Just nod when I hold one up. There you are. Can you reach to the window sill? You're watching the geese floating out there aren't you? A great one for the birds, our Lexie Moffat.

Lexie lets out a sudden, unbidden scream followed by a series of pig-like snorts and another scream. Cathy, the daycare assistant, strokes her arm to calm her and holds the plastic baby beaker towards her as a peace offering. Lexie screams again but wraps her knobbly fingers through the handle and sucks at the mouthpiece with her hardened gums. Later, in the greyness of the afternoon, Lexie Moffat cries.

**

Granny's voice, calling down the stairs. Then nothing. There were men come and said that she had to go into the sisters' room and kiss her Granny goodbye. She hadn't wanted to. She hadn't wanted her Granny to leave so she went and hid with the hens and watched from there but she can't now remember what she saw.

Senna's voice.

-   We can't go on. There's nothing left for us. I'm giving up the farm. You and Lexie will have to get us a place. Go to the Council.

A tiny house in town. No animals, not even a hen kept there. Senna gone too.

Walking back up the glen. Walking back into birch trees. Hot bannocks, cold water, always cold, fresh water.

Lexie sniffs. Puts her nose in the air and sniffs. Damp autumn woodland. Earth and mouldering and wood fires and a blanket wrapped around. Tea. She likes tea but nothing else. Cold water and tea.

Walking with her mother north and then west, house to house to farm to estate. Any job. Liking the animals better than scrubbing hearths. Working and walking. Away from the birch trees . New smells, dead smells to Lexie. New plantations and dank bogs. Bitter, foul, decaying things like deep winter when it turns warm too soon. Rotten seaweed piled up after a storm. Lexie screams.

**

A girl's voice at her side. Does she know her? She thinks she is a part of herself, somehow.

- Gran, how are you today?

A hand touches Lexie's arm. Lexie screams.

- Gran, come on, it's just baby Sandra come to see you. I've brought Paul too. You know us Gran, don't you?

Lexie screams but a little less fiercely.

- Look we've brought you in some pussy willow from beside the house. You would always cut it when we were wee and stroke it on our cheeks and tell us that there would soon be new lambs on the croft.

Sandra puts a sprig of the willow in her grandmother's hand and lifts her fingers to the soft grey buds.

Lexie screams a piercing, bilious scream, the pain of recognition, the pain of memory.

**

A ferry boat to the Islands. Her mother's voice.

> \- We'll take our chance, Lexie. The lambing starts soon. Plenty of work on the crofts and after that there will be hay cutting and the barley harvest and then the tattie lifting.

Robert MacKinnon smelled of rolling tobacco and whisky. Robert MacKinnon also smelled of something else – a raw acidic stink – the scent of a man in search of a woman.

The geese have tucked their heads under their wings and are bobbing gently. Lexie counts her fingers onto Sandra's arm. One, two, three four. One, two, three, four.

Screams, her mother screaming. He hurts her. Babies come but Lexie doesn't remember them. She had sheep. Her own lambs. They ate well. They stayed. He tried it with her but she ran. Ran away to her garden and her hens and her lambs. Always the smell of drink. Her mother's voice.

-       It keeps him from me, Lexie. More, he'll leave you alone. Just hide when his drinking pals are about. Hide. Hide.

Granny's voice.
-       Hide, hide, wee blot.

But why?
A warm smell of sheepswool pullover and moleskin breeks. Raider Moffat is beside her now. Holding her hand and asking her a question and he is lifting her carrying her. At last she is at Meanish.

James voice.
-       Because I'm a Borderer. It's what we did. The islanders think it funny so they call me Raider but I am your James, Lexie, and never forget that.

**

A kiss on her forehead. It can't be James. He had a beard, a red, coarse beard and he smelled of.....Not like this girl.

Her voice.

- Granny? Paul and I have to go now. We'll look in again on Friday. You can tell us what birds you've seen and whether the seals have come in.

Lexie screams.

Cathy. She knows Cathy who is there all the time. Cathy is an easy one. She smells of handwashing chemicals and something on her hair that Lexie doesn't know. Cathy's voice.

- Shall we move you up to the table?

Cathy releases the brake on the wheelchair and pushes Lexie into the small dining room. One, two, three. There is the man who always belches. He could be Robert MacKinnon. Would he be dead? Lexie doesn't know how many years it's been. The other lady, Mrs MacDonald, she knows from when they were in, when they were in something. Something she did with other old women after James had...

Mrs MacDonald, her singing.

- Tea for two, and two for tea, me for you and you....

Every teatime.

Lexie screams, Iain Dubh belches and curses and Kathleen MacDonald sings. Cathy moves between the chairs with a spoon.

**

Sitting in a chair at a fireside. Then laid gently on an old double bed with rust colouring its springs. In the back room. A scrubbed table and two chairs in the front with the hearth and a scullery off to one side. She telling him about sheep and birch trees and freshwater lochs and big game birds and how it was so cold you couldn't undress for whole weeks at a time or bits would drop off you. She whispering it into his ear when they were in the big double bed in the back room at Meanish.

Her mother had hugged her. Once. When was that?

Meanish, the croft at the end of the track, an island off an island. At high tide they were cut off, floating further westward and further away from the birches. Her voice.

- Tie a rope across to the main island, James. It'll anchor us if there's a storm.

He hugs her. Big arms about her, holding her together. The tickle of beard in her hair. He walks her to the shelter of her little walled garden. James' voice.

-        There's gannets, look Lexie, whiter than anything else. Shearwaters and guillemots and razorbills and...

Our boy. Sandy. Too wild to get across. We couldn't get him to. Doctor couldn't come. It happened so fast. His father's red hair. The storm.

We had a girl. I wanted Elizabeth. He called her Beattie. His mother, I think. Beattie at school, stayed away there. Too far for her each day. Unhappy she was. Always.

A teacher's voice.

-        Lexie McIlroy, will you please come here and sit still. University, Mrs McIlroy. Beattie could go to University. Can you not even get to ten? Say it again after me. She'll do well and you'll be so proud.

Alone, afloat. Lexie screams.

**

The girl. The one who comes. She has it. She is Sandra and she is the little girl who came every summer with her mother who didn't stay because she didn't like islands. But Sandra stayed all summer and sang and loved her and there was a boy, too. Beattie had a boy, too. They liked her garden and the lambs.

Beattie got married to another student. The dress, it showed her bump. Feckless girl.

Beattie's voice.

- We've already got a house in Dundee, Mum. Peter's father is a something. He has money. Don't need to live on an island and run a croft. It's different now. Come and stay.

Birch trees. Raider had taken her. She was sure it was Raider. White clean sheets, a huge white bath, white curtains, her best white nightgown. Gold shimmering in the trees, blue, silver, gold. Smell of autumn in the woods. Lexie cries and screams and hugs herself.

**

Cathy's voice.

- Mrs Moffat. That is quite enough for one day. You can't see those birds any longer now so shall we take you to your own room and get us some peace? You know there is nothing to be frightened of here and there are sending your own grandchildren away when they'd come specially to see you.

**

James' voice.
- We'll go home, Lexie. I didn't want to upset you. I thought you'd like to see where your family were laid. Do you not remember your Granny and Senna. You told me all about them.
Granny McIlroy, Auntie Senna and there was an uncle. Who was he? War. He died in the war. She's sure that was what they said. Never gave Senna children.

She hadn't slept in the crisp white sheets. It felt like being dead and wound around ready for her own funeral.

**

Cathy's voice.
- Now. Remember that it's Michael on the night shift and to pull your string if you need anything but I'll leave you the light on so you don't get frightened in the dark. Oh! Now hear

157

that is Kathleen MacDonald singing her heart out. Tiptoe through the Tulips indeed..... You'll have to let go of my sleeve. There now. Sweet dreams, Mrs M.

**

James' voice.

-    Where are you? I didn't say good.....I didn't... when you stopped being there. But it wasn't Meanish by then. I know we were in the flat. The School Hostel. Where Beattie had been. I remember. It was funny because we had a flat after it wasn't school any longer. Women came.
A woman's voice.

-    Sorry for your loss, Mrs Moffatt. He was a good man.

Walking into woodlands, soft underfoot and birdsong and drinking from the burns and washing in the lochs.

**

The rising howl of the wind. In her head the doors and window frames are knocking. The fire has burnt out. Day after day the storm hollers at them. She holds onto her head to still the fear. James trying to get out and lash the house together. Crash of water over the house. He comes to her and holds her. He holds her fast as the water rushes about their feet and holes appear in the roof. He holds her through the next day too when there is no let up. Tinned pears and baked beans. All they can find. It is gone. Lexie cries most for their sheep washed out to sea.

A voice in her head.

- You cannot stay. This place. It's too far off the map. We'll look after you.

Lexie Moffat wants to scream but at night she stuffs her fist in her mouth and they don't come. Sometimes they don't hear her when she tries to explain.

But James is here. She knows he is. He is always here. In the night she can hear him snoring but they must have given him a different bed because she can't ever seem to find his hand in the dark when she reaches out.

Later, though, when everyone else is asleep he will take her into the garden at Meanish and she'll tell him about the birch woodlands and he'll tell her the names of the birds.

31. The Doctor Will See You Now
by Gill Terry

In the gloomy waiting room Radio nan Gàidheal
bawls Scottish country dance tunes
through a speaker on the wall
apparently with no off switch.
A dozen plastic chairs in sheepshit green
encircle a vastness of lino,
but when the accordion embarks on The Gay
Gordons
nobody gets up to dance.

Katie Flora frets beside her tartan trolley
zipping and unzipping,
revealing what we already know:
she's been shoplifting at the Co again.
Murdo's stick is clamped between his boots
in case it strays like his old collie did.
He's chosen *Yachting World*
and holds it up before his face.
The pages, which he never turns,
flutter in a virtual ocean breeze.

Yellowing posters plead from pockmarked walls.
Does Somebody You Care For Drink Too Much?
How shall we count them all?
Would It Help To Talk To Someone?
Hardly, at this late stage, I fear.
See What Food Groups Should Be On Your Plate.
Does Katie Flora steal to order?
But my favourite, the one I love to
ponder as I wait: *You Have Your Own Bed,*
Why Die in Someone Else's?
Yes, indeed. Well, quite.

A long chord ends the Eightsome Reel.
My name is called. I rise,
bow slightly to my fellow dancers,
skip away.

32. Island...Life
by Jane Verburg

A beech falls. Uprooted in the night winds. Smashes across the path and scatters its branches down to the shoreline. No one hears it.

Kyle flicks his hair, the smell of iodine and old folk is hard to shake. Wanders towards home to the sound of the chimney-pot gulls. Jo will be up, he thinks, and decides to avoid her, he'll grab the dog and walk up the Braehead. No point in meeting this early.

Lydia stares intensely at the photograph and back to her canvas. Then finishes painting the nose of the pale, long-haired retriever. She longs for a cup of tea. Jasper stirs at her feet and asks to be let out. She strokes his ears and stands.

Kenny stumbles out of the house and loads the van – diesel cans, lifejackets, spare wellies. The weather's fine after the night winds. The forecast good. Southwesterlies 3 – 4. The sea looks calm enough. There'll be plenty of punters today. Keen to see the seals. Maybe they'll be lucky and a dolphin will jump. Maybe not.

Calum lets the needle fall. He holds his vein shut. Calm lifts him.

Myrtle-the-ferry pulls on her steel-toe capped boots and squashes her double-G bust into her workman's overalls. Hopefully the poppers will hold. She looks up at the sky and says aloud, 'I'll deserve that pint tonight.'

An alarm rings. Ryan checks the time. If I'm quick I'll avoid breakfast and can run for the early bus, he thinks. Can't cope with the endless questions that stream out of his step-mum as she stuffs toasts into the little ones. Can't cope with the whys and whens and what ifs.

Ishbel longs for a conversation with Ryan. Just a few friendly words between them would help. Can't stand his sullen morning face much longer. She needs to talk to him about his latest girlfriend. She needs to brave the subject of love and contraception and how easy it is to ruin your life and does he realise that he can't just keep using the place like a hotel and how *is* he doing at school; this is his life they're talking about. Or not talking about.

Jo quickly deletes the Google search history as she hears the door and knows that Kyle will collect the dog and be gone. If she stays upstairs at least she'll not have to see him, smell him. She closes down the Secondlife tab and clears her throat.

Ryan checks his pockets – phone, condoms, e-tabs, cash – and heads out along Shore Street for the bus. He'll hide out at Tasha's again today. No doubt at some point school will contact his step-mum but for now...

Jasper reads the grass. Knows who's been here already today and cocks his leg at a rose bay willow herb. Jauntily strides off towards the Braehead path. Lydia follows. Wonders if she should ring the hospital again today and speak to the consultant. Dad's explanations don't add up.

It's six months since Willie-the-fish threw soil onto his father's coffin up on the hill. Six months since he took over the boat *Skyline*. He unties the bowline and takes the rope aboard. His head aches. The creels will be bursting today. He knows. He can tell. The night winds will have brought in the squats and tonight he'll be in the hotel buying the drinks for once.

Calum, surprisingly energetic and with no shakes, wanders down to the harbour. Catches a glimpse of the new young lassie who's moved into the Manse. She sees him and smiles. Almost stops to flirt. What the hell's she doing out at this time in the morning. She half waves to him. Maybe my luck's in, he thinks.

Emma runs on from the harbour towards the Manse. She'll just sneak in before her mother wakes and no one will be any the wiser about where she spent the night. Perfect.

Kyle watches the ferry pull out. Willie-the-fish, already heading out to sea, must have been early today. And Kenny's rib is already off the mooring. Kyle heads across the Links. Sees the early dog walkers. Blethers a wee bittie about the weather being fine and takes the lower path to the Braehead.

Emma's mother hears her daughter creep up the back stairs. She pulls the white duvet around her and reaches for her pills. So much easier to pretend she hasn't heard a thing.

Donald arrives at the shop before it has opened. He feels sure he's come for a reason. Starts rummaging through his pockets looking for a list. Surely he's come for the messages.

'Morning, Granda.'

'Morning? Is it morning?'

Donald does not recognise Calum, his grandson.

Wictoria and Jack look at each other and smile. Another contract signed. Just so long as staffing stays constant, just so long as Janice stays with them, all will be well. This is just the beginning. The beginning of good times.

The thrush hits Ishbel's car with a low thud. She sees it tumble away in the wing mirror. Rushing to work.

Natalie is chuffed to bits with her new bowl. The mermaids and lighthouses make her smile. She pops it into the boot before heading towards the Seal Trip shed. She deserves a wee treat now that Ben has finally moved out. Not a pair of boxers left.

Jo can't stop herself logging in again. Davina has become part of her. She longs to make Davina's choices. Choices that take Davina to places that Jo would never go; do things Jo would never do.

Kyle steps over the fallen beech. Hardly notices it. Doesn't wonder how many rings sit within its trunk or who lived here when it was a sapling. And as he steps over its torn, brown body something nags at his mind and makes him think that he and Jo need to talk. He isn't quite sure what about but he knows she's distracted these days. No longer connected to him. The dog picks up the scent of a deer. An unfinished rainbow arches over the water and an oystercatcher screeches and turns south.

Lydia hears the same bird and winces. She returns home and tells Steph that there's a fallen tree and she'd best go and see to it in case there's some firewood to be had. When she's gone Lydia lifts the phone and calls the hospital. 'It's my father, I need to talk to someone about my father.'

Tasha watches the thin blue circle confirm her pregnancy.

Calum returns home for another hit.

Jasper sits at Lydia's feet. Then licks her face as she holds her head in her hands and cries. She lets the dog warm her and then logs on and starts to search for ferry times and flights south. She'd better stay up tonight and complete the retriever commission; she might not be back for a while. If it weren't for Jasper she might not be back at all.

Out at sea Willie curses each empty creel. A rain shower flattens the cat's paws.

Etta stamps her foot by the back door. 'I'll not go to big school. Never. Mrs MacLean works there and she's a coo. A big, fat coo.' Janice rolls her eyes at her daughter and notices that the swallows are gathering on the wires. She goes inside, pushes Etta to one side. Sitting down at her old, grey computer she orders school uniform, shoes, pencils, colouring pens, a winter coat. Etta is happy outside playing with the hens; cooing and clucking at them. When the extra cost of island postage is added Janice goes back and deletes the coat. Finally she checks her emails. 'Title: Job offer' catches her eye ... and there it is. They want her. They're willing to train her and they'd like her to start within the month. Janice suddenly scoops in some air. She'll need to start planning. Cancel the school uniform, cancel the rent, book ferries, hire a van, hand in her notice, find a new school, find a new home. A new home. This really is her ticket out. She dials Lydia's number.

Myrtle-the-ferry orders her third pint and whisky chaser, glances across at Billy asleep on the bar, his face squashed and tied. 'Fancy another?' Billy looks up. 'Aye, if you're buying'. Kenny and the boys are at the pool table.

Steph returns home with another wheel barrow full of logs. She stacks them up. They'll season over the winter. Just like the rest of us.

Ryan catches his usual bus back and heads for Calum's.

Myrtle orders another. And her poppers eventually give way. She bustles out and staggers home.

Alan bolts the door. Kenny and the boys head up the road and Billy trips on the step as he leaves. Grazes his hand along the wall as he regains his balance. He'll just take a final look at *Skyline*.

An owl calls from the oak tree Etta's grandmother carved her initials into one full moon night.

Willie trips again.

When the final falls comes there is almost no sound to it. Strange to think that the weight of a man's body might not cause a splash.

A seal lifts its head above the waves and curves back down.

It is Kenny who finds him. Next morning. His body caught between the ferry and the fishing boats. Face down.

33. Holiday Home
by Morag Henriksen
(Psalm 103 vv 15, 16 metrical version)

This house is grey with age
and lonely in retirement.
Storm windows arch their eyebrows in surprise
when we unlock the door.
The kitchen floor
is spongy underfoot
and rust has crept along the shelves
where scones and pancakes
used to fill the tins.
A Royal Baking Powder can
behind the drop-down flap
captures infinity inside the cabinet.
Blue mildew sticks the pages of the Bibles
and godly Sabbath reading.

Left as it was when Auntie Mary died,
the house still offers hospitality.
The dishes in the good room are dust-free.
No spiders loom the corners.
But the neighbour's care
can't halt decay.

Although the calendars and clock stand still
Time will not let it be.
Seals on the reef outside
clock up the movements of the tide
and mark the flow of time.

34.   The Boatshed
by Maureen MacKenzie

The shafts of shining dust always suggest his presence, twirling and mingling with the smell of varnish, wood-shavings and a whiff of tobacco. He is, however, long gone and this can only be a trick of memory or imagination.

The corrugated iron roof is broken in patches allowing beams of sunlight to play on the beams of wood straddling the roof and the planks waiting to be crafted on the earthen floor. The open rafters host an assortment of chain and rope, and, folded neatly in a dark corner, are the sails of the Màiri Bhàn, his pre-war pride and joy.

The dry-stone walls originally enclosed his grandfather's house and the blocks are soaked with the emotions and stories of generations. Boulders have been infiltrated by ferns, forming a sea of fronds ready to launch the unfinished boat.

In one corner lies a jumble of household detritus accumulated over the best part of two centuries: an old kitchen cabinet, enamel jugs, a ratchet for frightening sheep. Like a surreal sculpture welded by layers of dust. Not the symbolic decay of Miss Havisham's wedding feast but the evidence of many busy lives.

Crofting implements merit a corner of their own; great scythes jostle with peat cutters and a weight for whelks tells a tale of sore backs and hard times. Alongside, an ancient carpenter's chest is crumbling, spilling out rough saws and vices and chunky planes. Wooden templates for keels, transoms and gunnels rest against them and join the fusion of wood, leather and rusting iron.

A wood-steamer is allocated its own special extension, jutting out from the square shape of the shed. Its brick oven leads to the steam box where larch was made pliable to form the ribs of the craft. Now it houses abandoned birds' nests and a cosy corner for the cat on a winter's night.

In centre stage, like a pharaoh's sarcophagus, lie the remains of his unfinished work. The central block supports a keel and a klinker kilt of pleated planks that no-one has the heart to dismantle. His premature departure left the boats rib-less and life-less and his sons were not old enough to carry on his craft. A shiny brass nameplate 'MacKenzie and Son' rests against a fraying ball of calking cotton. The plaques were handed down generation by generation, master to apprentice, each 'son' eventually becoming the 'MacKenzie'. But he would be the last 'son' and the last 'MacKenzie'.

The workbench is cluttered with evidence of toil and the spill-over of ordinary life: copper nails (a pound a pound), a Tilley lamp, war medals in a tea tin, Greenshield stamps and a piece of an old chanter. Nothing was thrown away – even old treacle jars were recycled to hold nails by screwing their lids to the underside of the shelf above the bench. Postcards from old pleasure boats, worked by his brother, hang like barely recognisable ghosts from large nails. Did he envy his brother's move to the big city while he stayed on the croft with his mother? His only view of the wider world was as a territorial holding the fort at St Valery and being transported across Europe in a cattle wagon. His travels and his war were over in nineteen forty.

At least he was spared the shipyards of Gdansk; his crofting home gave him an alternative occupation to offer his captors and he spent the war as a prisoner on a Polish farm. Not so bad, but enough to make status symbol such as sailing boats redundant and advocate peace at any cost. He was happy for the Mairi Bhan to be given to two Polish soldiers who wanted to sail to a home that no longer existed. At forty, he himself came back, and as the steamer turned at the Big Head, he saw the Cuillin, his croft-house and his shed – all as he had left them. Only he had changed.

But his life was just beginning. Old baby shoes on a shelf – one (left or right) for each of his four children – and his additions to the household rubbish collection are testament to a life eventually fulfilled: a handmade, hooded cradle and simple barred cots are filled with bundles of shinty sticks and old seventy eight gramophone records.

The launching door swings open and his grandchildren spill in. Despite being warned of the dangers, it is a place of adventure and exploration. The shed is once again full of noise and activity and the dust on the work-bench spirals in a sparkling spindrift before swooping and dipping to tell its tale.

35. A Door in My House
by Ian Stephen

There's a door in my house I don't want to open.
There's an archive inside.
Some people may want access but
if I open that door I know
the papers needed for the tax return
the prints and printouts
the tickets, used and not
the books that mattered so much at a time;
cibachromes and transparencies;
digital examples, quality in their day –
and all indeed components of
a single film.
They'll all flood out.

You're talking to a man they think is fearless,
my crews I mean,
when waters run large off Port of Ness
break hard and high on the Bragg
and suck so low around the bun that's sweet Rockall
amass at the turn of the tide south of Arklow
stand up to speak to you at the race of Mey.
I think in these circumstances my voice gives
confidence

but I'm having difficulty opening that door.

A broach is when you lose the grasp of physics
when your keel, whatever shape, does sweet f. all.
The forward section digs deep
and the arse end lifts,
offering itself,
in a way that must be sexy
to distant observers.

You ask to dump the sheet
which means
please take all that tension away.
And if that's done in time
all that happens is a lot of spray.

The show depends on wires that stay the mast
another way the aggro can remove itself –
destruction that refrains from total loss.

But if you're lucky, there's a long low moan
a shudder from the boat's pumping self

and that relief can happen if
I turn the bloody handle of that door.

36. "The Fair Isle Jumper"
(Oil on canvas, Stanley Cursitor 1887-1976)
by Mary Robinson

It's your face I notice –
light smudging cheekbone
and neck, a little shine
on your nose,
eyes dark with pleading,
lips stubborn – what is the word
you hold in your mouth?

That crazy-patterned sweater,
a charcoal grey scarf (did he drape that?)
and white gloves, one worn
one held, as if you are on the brink
of a decision.
Your jasmine scent mingles
with linseed and tobacco.

Do you know he keeps your face
with his paints? A cut-out head
so you can be popped into a picture
even when you aren't there.

37.   Northern Lights
by Gill Terry

He called her Lavender Mermaid - just in his head, you understand, not to her face: that would have been crazy. Lavender because she kept telling her patients to take relaxing baths with lavender oil and Mermaid because she was fond of the spa in the local gym and of taking beach holidays in the Med.

She was middle-aged and heavy and though she liked to wear drop earrings and chakra bracelets on each wrist she used little makeup and her fingernails were professionally short. Her caramel hair was long and curly and it splayed across her shoulders like a bridal veil. But nobody could call her vain - except perhaps in her reluctance to put on in public the little pair of reading specs she'd recently had to buy.

She liked to talk, as much about herself as about her patients and, generous with her time, she always, always overran. You could tell when she was consulting because it would be standing room only in the pine-clad waiting room within the Scandinavian chalet that was the surgery in Kinlochaird. She had a loyal, if stoical, following in the island population but word had spread: you asked to see another partner if you were in a hurry or just wanted a nod and a packet of pills.

It was not surprising, then, that his consultation when it came was unconventional. When he finally told her what was happening inside his head - stuff that would have had most GPs reaching for the telephone as well as the prescription pad - 'Discussion' was all she wrote in his notes. For his protection, she said. Then she got out her Post-It notes, wrote 'Charlotte' and her home phone number on a slip and handed it to him.

'Keep this in a safe place and use it if you need to, John. Any time.'

* * *

It was early spring and bookings for the coming season at John Rennie's guest house were desperately thin. At first he'd thought that he was simply anxious, obsessed with the finances, not getting enough sleep. He had even wondered if the male menopause was real and if, at fifty, he might be a candidate.

He wished now that he'd made more of an effort when they'd first arrived to make friends with his neighbours, but he'd treated the crofters' wives and their seasonal B&Bs as competitors - that's how it was done where he came from, after all - and when his Vacancies sign had disappeared one night he'd wondered if it really was the gale that had taken it.

'And why, exactly, do they all have binoculars on their window sills trained in our direction?'

'Let it go, John,' said Sally, when he was still hammering on about it a week later. But he couldn't, could he? Eventually he'd let Sally go instead, away in the Range Rover five hundred miles South to a place when the sun sometimes shone even in November, and the wind didn't howl every night.

'Just a temporary separation while we consider our options,' she'd said. Yeah, right.

It was two months later that John finally recognised his worsening symptoms for what they truly were. The over-analysis of every word he heard, the connections he made that defied conventional logic, the all-pervading sense of dread. Everything was relevant and everything was about *him*. It was exhausting.

What's more, something was trying to reach him from another planet. Angels had chosen him for a task and there was important information that only he could decode. It was just a question of figuring it all out but he'd tried and tried and still he couldn't make sense of it. He retreated inside his head deep within his thinking and now, increasingly, he hated coming out.

He hadn't slept properly for weeks. His ears were filled with a mosquito-like whining which he reckoned to be the noise of electrical current as it flowed through the house wiring. Even when he buried his head in his pillows he could still hear the electrons moving. Sometimes he'd be woken by the doorbell but when he went to check there was never anybody there. A heron might rise, shrieking its complaint when he switched on the outside light, but nothing more.

Insight. He'd always had plenty of insight. That treacherous little word. He knew *exactly* what was happening to him now, he knew what would happen next, and he knew he needed help.

A normal doctor would be useless, but there was just a chance that the remarkable Lavender might have something new to say. He owed it to himself at least to try. So he wrote her a letter and dashed out in the middle of the night to shove it through the surgery's letterbox before he changed his mind. He asked her to look at the parts of his medical records that covered his teenage years. There'd be something relevant there. The street lamps flickered on and off as he sneaked past. 'We're watching you,' they said.

* * *

It was the time between five pm and eight which was the hardest, the hours she had to be careful always to fill. That was why she was an early evening regular at the gym. It was quiet then, too, so she was less likely to end up sharing the sauna with a patient. Not that she really minded. In this village where everyone knew everyone, bumping into patients was an inevitability she had accepted. Kinlochaird was not like Chelmsford.

'Hi, Charlotte,' said one of them now as she pounded the treadmill at little more than walking pace.

'Hello Duncan. How's it going?' she managed between heavy breaths. Maybe she should get headphones like the kids.

Ach, the kids. She missed them like crazy.

John tried to keep the car moving at a reasonable speed but it was hard to go fast and still read the number plates on the vehicles coming the other way. And God forbid that he should miss one: you could never tell when it might matter. Just recently the letters with spiky bits had become quite repulsive. The letter 'Y' was especially hard to bear.

He drove to the far end of the supermarket car park where a grassy bank separated the tarmac from the frothy grey waves six feet below. He let the engine idle while he watched a red creel boat bob drunkenly on its mooring, then parked up close to the building so that he could trail his hand along the brickwork until he reached the door.

After that there'd be a trolley to hold on to and it wouldn't be too bad. In the biscuit aisle the graphics on the packaging shouted up at him. 'Nazi!' screamed the bourbons, 'Nazi! Nazi!' He took the gingernuts instead.

'Cheerio just now,' trilled the checkout lady. Even that was a puzzle.

Back home in the safety of his room he fired up his laptop and put 'bourbons Nazi' into Google: 160,000 hits. He wasn't surprised. It could take a while, but he'd find the right page eventually. But God, he was so tired of all this.

It was seven o' clock and Charlotte had been home for less than five minutes when the phone rang. It was Lachie: She *would* be there that evening? Yes, of course she would. But she couldn't blame him for checking. She'd missed their last meeting and that put everything in doubt.

She didn't take the car. No need for anyone to see it parked there and put two and two together. So she put on her long woollen coat and her fleece gloves, and pulled her pink ski-hat - from Denver: was that just two years ago? - low over her ears and headed out into the frost. Lachie was waiting under the street lamp beside the building, his breath steaming like a kettle into the orange glow.

'C'mon, *a ghràidh*, let's get into the warm.' He put his arm in hers and with his other pushed open the heavy wooden door.

There was a good turnout - maybe ten or twelve folk, which wasn't bad considering the weather. There were a couple of seats left for them in the small circle, and once they'd settled themselves Calum called the meeting to order.

'Who wants to go first?' he said, not looking anyone directly in the eye. Charlotte took a deep breath, gave a little sigh and got to her feet.

'Hello, my name's Charlotte, and I'm an alcoholic.'

It was nearly midnight in the Seaview Guest House and John sat in his office with just the glow from his laptop screen to break the darkness. Outside the rising winds moaned and whistled around the dormers and began to rattle the roof tiles. It was going to be a rough few hours.

He felt himself sliding away towards the abyss. Time and space. He needed to get a grip on time and space. If he could keep hold of those two he would still be in the world: he would still exist. So he gathered up all the clocks he could find and set them where he could see them in his room. Tomorrow he would buy more off the internet. He sat on the carpet in the corner where he could brace himself between two walls and the floor. He'd put a talk programme on the radio and switch his desk lamp on, and that way he might just make it through the night.

One a.m., and Charlotte sat at the breakfast bar in her kitchen staring into space and contemplating the bottle that she knew was in the left-hand cupboard beneath the sink, in a Co-op carrier just behind the Pledge.

She'd let the unpaid bills mount up and if she didn't pay the phone bill soon they'd cut her off. And then there was the pile of Lancets underneath her bed. So many articles she should have read by now.

She was exhausted but sleep rarely came, even with the pills. She had no more holiday due until June and if she asked for an extra day they'd all look at her sideways and suspect the worst. She had to be so careful. Alistair was still reporting on her to the GMC. That embarrassing little interview each month when he ushered her into his consulting room and pretended to care. As if she would admit to *him* that things had gone pear-shaped again. And then there was Lachie. There was a road she really must not go down - but it was so hard when all the good men were already taken and the nights were long and lonely in Kinlochaird.

'Enough!'

She walked out into the night leaving the door wide open and followed the yellow street lights past the fishery pier, where the rigging on the prawn boats jangled and clanked, and on towards the cantilever bridge that spanned the churning waters of the kyle.

He could have sworn he'd heard a dog barking but he found nothing in the guest house car park when he looked. Two a.m.. Hours and hours to go before daylight, yet there *was* colour and movement in the sky. Eerie green shapes like angels dancing, angels beckoning. He had to follow!

He found her in the middle of the bridge. She'd already crossed the barrier and was sitting on a concrete buttress twenty yards above the sea. He clambered down to reach her and like a child she let him take her by the hand.

'Safe now.'

The flickering lights of the aurora filled the Northern sky. John felt the photons soar through space and stuff his brain with understanding. As they huddled together, still and silent and waiting for daybreak, the answers to a thousand questions hurtled frame by frame across his mind. The sea, black and glinting like hammered metal, billowed gently under sinking winds as the clamour of the storm died down.

38. The Boodie and the Five o' Clock Friend
by Suzie A. Kelly

> *An' see na ye that braid road*
> *Down by yon sunny fell?*
> *Yon's the road the wicked gae,*
> *An' that's the road to hell.*

from 'The Queen of Elfan's Nourice', Child Ballad No. 40

I believe I'm going to kill myself.

And now we ride the postbus to where the Atlantic will swallow us. The snaking single-track road leads from the ferry terminal in Lochmaddy, along the west coast machair, to the stone causeways of Benbecula. We're going the long way round. I've not been here long. There's no collection of people who'll miss me, but perhaps my neighbours will notice when my curtains never close.

Your stubby claws grip my shoulder. 'I'm worried you'll change your mind,' you say in low-register whispers. You change position and flit to my other shoulder. I assure you I've taken care of everything: we are good to go. I cancelled the direct debits last week.

I need the white noise to stop: the yackety-yak of unpaid bills, withdrawn housing benefit, and you. You sulk at this. Yes, you are, you're sulking. Your stone lips pout. You are a grotesque: a devilish half-gargoyle/half-bird with yellowing horns and scraggy black feathers. Like me, poor Boodie, you've seen better days.

We're tucked into the second row of grey seats. I coorie into the side-window and hide. A tweed 'Shopping Day' hat pokes over the edge of the headrest in front. I listen to its owner. Her voice lilts across the front space, making communion with the postbus driver, Mairead Anna . I assume she's off to the big shop in Benbecula.

The women discuss the weather. Their conversation, in the island's home tongue, sounds violent and passionate to the outsider's ear. But, what single English word could describe rain like today, this rain that stings your face like a thousand needles? What other language would do it justice, if not Gàidhlig?

'Scots?' you say and wink.

I ignore the jibe.

The tourist in the single seat to our left is wrapped in a Gore-tex shroud. He distracts himself from the female chatter by fiddling with the zip on his backpack.

'Wild camping in November? He's mad too,' you say.

I think he just feels out of place; another intruder in the rolling peat lands. No matter.

I smile to myself, in the small, secret space you haven't yet taken over: the ladies just feel the cold and are wary of the coming gale season.

'You came all the way from Kilmarnock for chat like this?' you carp.

I will you to be quiet; to allow me room to breathe. Yes, I know you won't. You can't. But, you forget there are as many flavours of rain here in the Uists as there are winds. If you stay here year-round, this connection with the island leaches into your bones. People survive and thrive here in spite of the damnation of the wild elements that influence their peat cutting, animal feeding, fishing, planting, washing, working, driving, schooling and even internet; which they lose altogether when the southwesterlies strike. So you see, talking about the weather is an art form here: a Hebridean sound sculpture. Weather matters.

You're not convinced. You fold your patchy stone arms. You're still sulking. Yes, you are. I know you as well as you know me.

You pad round to study the view outside. I follow your gaze, past the chipped window glass, to the scattered rocks and rusted heather beyond. My head feels packed with cotton wool.

We bounce gently with the suspension, the steady engine noise seducing us, and I see winter has stolen the clean, white swans from their lochans. No bedraggled-looking fishing parties huddle around the pebbled shorelines. Even the geese have abandoned us. The Uibhisteachs are left to withstand the fierce months ahead without them. And we would have been so cold. And so wet. And...I feel out my use of the past tense. Is it odd that it's not odd?

You flare your nostrils and your arms slip down to your belly.

As we round the Sollas bends, my thoughts feel finite. They come in scattered, unregulated snippets. Time shrinks away the closer we get to the sea.

The material world is bathed in a late-Autumnal light that is uncomfortably shiny and unreal, as if the volume on the world is turned up just that little bit too loud.

Mairead Anna pulls us into a passing place to allow Fergus's coal lorry to grunt past. I know his face, but we haven't met. The interruption allows them to pause their conversation for a while, and we're given back to the grumbling engine. In the human quiet, I swallow my internal world in case my brokenness leaks out. I couldn't bear the weight of labelling, of being constructed as 'ill'. You're unconcerned.

The western coastline of Vallay rattles into view and the sky lightens as a moment of blue sky breaks through the cumulus. The cliffs by Hosta are close.

When the grey resumes, you ask about our journey's end.

'Are you scared?'

I meet the fire-ringed black holes of your eyes and confess I find the concept of 'not being' strange. I've practised 'being' for thirty-seven years and soon ...

'You know there's no other side: no gods seeking retribution or explanation?' you say, crouching down on my woollen cardigan.

I nod. I understand the concept of nothingness: no worries; no 'me'; just void space.

'You'll fight against the salt water when it first takes you,' you say.

I say, a fisherman once told me that when your lungs fill up, once they're full and you've stopped kicking out, peace takes over.

'You understand that the white light is just your retinas burning out…that there's no karmic re-birth?'

Again, I agree.

'Imagine that! Imagine suffering the indignity of crawling from another bloody caul to start life all...over...again. Urgh, the mess and trouble...,' you squawk in fright. You ruffle your feathers.

I wonder if we're doing the right thing and you hop up to my face.

'What's to stop you? Nobody cares enough to try...'

I know.

'...and Andrew left you in his mind long before he left you physically...'

He found it hard, I reason back. The babies came so early. At ten weeks there's only blood to mark their existence - so much blood and no soft, new-born flesh to cradle against his skin. Or my breasts.

'Remember what he said? He said, "They're no' babies, Juliette, just cells". He said that while packing his suitcase, remember?'

The ache spills through my arms. You mimic him so well.

'Well, he got a one-way ferry trip to the mainland and you got the obnoxious quiet of a three-bedroom semi. He'll not be back to claim you...'

I breathe out; long and slow.

We pass blighted croft houses in between the old white ones and the new eco-friendly ones. Although the townships are dormant, the occasional working dog patrols its own driveway.

'So, we do it now?' you say. 'We'll leave all your hurts and complications behind for good. Yes?'

I agree and you hunker back into the softness of my cardigan.

Everything is mapped out and straightforward.

And, here we are. Mairead Anna pulls into another passing place and parks us alongside a red postbox all on its own on the moor; a good walk away from the troop of scattered houses who use it. Mairead Anna unbuckles her seatbelt and reaches over the dashboard to pick up her jangle of keys and an electronic postal device.

'Ceart, ma-thà,' she says. 'Wait an' I'll get the door for you, Juliette…'

This makes the air go lighter into my lungs: she knows me.

I mumble my gratitude as Mairead Anna clambers into the passenger side and hauls open the stiff side door. The cold wheeze from the Atlantic coast floods in. I stand up and then force of habit makes me panic about where I've left my handbag. Where is it? Did it fall under the seat? I start to check and then you remind me.

'Whatever would you need one of those for?' you cackle, steadying yourself on the beads of my necklace.

Of course.

I nod goodbye to the other passengers: he nods back, while she emits a cheery, 'Tìoraidh an-dràsta'. I thank Mairead Anna again and clamber down from the bus. She re-starts the engine and guns along the road, chasing the sunset.

The gate to the beach track lies open. Waves crack into foam nearby.

We can do this, can't we?

'Yes, yes,' you say.

Peat reek fights through the wind to reach us on the path to Tràigh Stir. The rain resumes: a listless spattering of droplets. Soon, in the half-light, we reach the cliff. Not quite the edge of the world, but close enough. St Kilda broods in the distance.

I don't know if I can do this, now we're here. I hear the roaring green ocean and feel shell-sand below my feet. Seaweed dances beneath the froth like the hair of a drowned girl. I step back.

You're outraged. 'You must do this…you must! There's no way out…just jump!'

My throat tightens. The Autumn light fades. You're right. There's no other way.

I inch to the edge again and dangle a foot over when a strange female voice bleeds into the afternoon.

'There is another way…'

'Get her away!' you shout.

My stomach cramps. I turn to the land and to face her. The old woman leans against the sheep fence, her shopping bag resting on wet sand. Straight white hair dangles from beneath her tweed hat.

'It's you? It's not what it looks like…,' I protest.

'Oh, I think it is,' she says. 'I'm glad I followed you.'

'Get away from us, witch!' you scream. Ancient fires blaze from the back of your eyes.

'Isd, dirty Boodie! Call me no such thing!'

You spit rage at her.

'You can see him?' I say.

'Of course, and what a cruel, insistent creature he is as well!'

You curse her. She waves a gloved hand and you're unable to speak. You flit from shoulder to shoulder. You would stab her in the eye with her own hat pin, if you could. You grab onto my beads again and urge me back towards the cliff. With every morsel of wrath, you will this to happen before night swoops in.

'I'm sorry,' I tell her. 'It's too hard…'

'What if you threw him off instead?'

197

'Oh, I could never hurt him.'

You stop fluttering and stand heroically, hands balled on your hips, daring her to continue.

'But, he's hurting you...'

'He can't help it...'

You smirk.

'I'm too late, then. Am I?' she asks.

'Yes. I'm sorry.' I feel weary to my marrow.

I think she's about to leave, but instead she pushes her glasses up her

nose and addresses me directly, 'You know he was never going to jump with you, don't you?'

'What?'

You scream in silence as she plants doubts in my mind.

I look to you. You were coming with me, weren't you?

You look away.

You weren't going to let me do it alone, were you?

You can't meet my eyes.

The old woman checks her watch as the tide attacks the rocks below.

'It's five o'clock, mo charaid. Perhaps you'll come for tea and leave this business for another day? Hm? I live nearby...'

I stand in the rain, confused and bereft. You're the last thing I can lose. I'm defeated.

You babble inside my head and haul on my necklace one last time. I rip it off and tie it around your thick stone neck to choke you. You fight back. The more I choke you, the more your black feathers fade to grey and I feel brighter; more alive than before. Well, to the sea with you! And I fling you with all my might into the Atlantic, but keen softly as you tumble and claw at the beads around your throat.

You're swallowed whole.

'Glè mhath!' the old woman claps.

I feel a pang at your passing. She takes my hand, but I can't bear to leave. You're still part of me.

'I should go to him.'

'Nonsense. He'd never do it for you.'

I drop her hand. 'I want him back…'

'We'll talk by the fire,' she says.

She leads me through the peat reek to a blackhouse down an unfamiliar track. A fir tree grows out its roof. I wonder if it's damp inside. The brickwork is crumbling and the front-door hangs half-off its hinges. Smoke burps from the chimney pot and candles flicker on the inside of the window pane. She's home.

'Come in to the warmth,' she says.

She drags open the shabby wooden door and drops her shopping bag on the dirt floor inside. From the doorway, I can see a dry single room with a gnarled tree trunk growing through the centre. It's encircled by wooden shelves stacked with multi-coloured glass bottles; some labelled and some not. All are full. Garlands of herbs are strung across the beams. Crocheted patchwork blankets line the chairs and the single bed against the back wall. Something in the large cardboard box snores by the open fire and two ginger paws stretch out from inside it.

She wanders over to her tea things and drops dried leaves from a canister into a cup. She pours in hot water from the fire kettle.

'Are you for coming inside with us?' she asks.

'I better not,' I say, pulling away.

Her shoulders droop. 'We were looking forward to the company. We rarely get the craic this far out...'

'I'm sorry,' I say, 'Truly.'

She tuts. She flips her glasses onto her head and walks towards me with the hot tea.

'Drink!' she says.

I take it and sip the woody liquid. This isn't normal tea, but I welcome it. The warmth spreads through me.

She hovers by her doorway. 'You still want that creutair dubh?'

'I'm lost without him.'

'Well,' she sighs, 'return to the path. He's outside drying his feathers by the byre.

He'll not come past the gate.'

'Really? I haven't lost him?'

'Not yet.'

I smile and make my goodbyes. She makes me promise to return at the same time next week. I thank her for her kindness in noticing me and leave the teacup with her.

The rain has cried itself out now. You're frowning outside.

Boodie?

You turn your back. It'll be a long night. But, next week, when I meet my five o'clock friend, she will listen and I will learn while you tend your wings. Yes, you and I will dance this dance again. But, when we do, I'll gain a little more strength while you grow a little weaker, and a little shabbier, and a little easier to override.

Come. If we hurry, we'll make the evening postbus. And, so you come with me as you always do.

39.   The Muse
by Val Fellows

Lachie made his third coffee of the morning, gazing out of the window whilst the kettle boiled; something after all might appear on the horizon. But it never did, the horizon was merely the faintest line dividing sea from sky; today, as always, grey from grey. He sighed, transferred his hopes to the imminent arrival of the post; but that too, proved uneventful. He kicked the dog out to chase imaginary rabbits, checked his emails; his diary re-affirmed his worst fears – nothing.

What, he thought, did the great writers do when in this intolerable situation – comparable to being in a state of unrequited love? Lachie stared at the bookshelves, willing a title to glow, incandescent, and illumine his mind. But it didn't. What about Wikipedia – surely something there?

Yes! A muse, that's what I need, in line with ancient tradition - wonder if it still works?

His father had been a fisherman, practical, yet superstitious; his mother a would-be artist who died two years ago; he had not yet cleared out her 'studio' – the old byre, so he strode out purposefully, rattled and pushed the door open, convinced he would find something inspirational there.

Rummaging through boxes of unclassified plaster casts, he came upon the head of a woman, hair twined round her head and a faraway look in her eye. Lachie snatched her up, kissed her white lips and carried her off triumphantly. He set her down next to his computer screen, to the left of the keyboard and seriously began his wooing. She seemed non-plussed. Lachie dusted her, tilted her head in order that she might take in the view, set a buttercup amidst her cold curls – and waited.

He made soup, didn't notice the sinister dark blotches on the bread, and sat, poised at the keyboard, waiting for inspiration to strike. It didn't. He was perplexed: had no experience of 'the fairer sex' – what should he do? She looks a bit pale, he thought; muses must surely embody, yes, express the passion of life itself?

Lachie was aware that he was becoming dangerously close to profane ideas: a voice reproved him - "stop now, while you can" – but, he didn't want to; it was exciting … He was following his intuition, it seemed to prompt him, ignite ideas, it somehow bade him follow; as in his boyhood, when, lost in the long grasses, he was somehow in his element.

Now, he was shuffling items around in his mother's dressing table drawer, a kind of blind searching; when you know something will turn up, and be right, whatever it is. Lachie found himself swivelling her rose-red lipstick - the kiss of life. He carefully applied it to his pale-faced lady, his muse; then stepped back to appraise the effect. A slap in the face: she looked even paler. No eye contact – her eyes were vacant – he returned to the drawer, found some green eye shadow and a brush; set to work with a fervour unknown in his other creative efforts. Then he wanted to colour her hair: what would suit? An Andy Warhol blond didn't seem right, so he used a coppery nail polish, which added a life-like lustre. He was pleased: - only a name was missing.

Then I'm finished, he thought; beginning to feel tired – the dog wanting fed and the chickens on the loose again. 'Mairi' – I shall call her 'Mairi', he exclaimed out loud, draping a daisy chain around her neck. Quite exhausted by his artistic endeavours, Lachie attended to his more menial daily chores, and eventually went to bed without the vaguest concern about writing his novel; tomorrow would do.

Tomorrow arrived with an unusually clear sky, and the surprise arrival of the post van; moreover, a new post-lady stepped out. 'It's Lachlan Macdonald I'm looking for', she said.

'That's me, sure enough … are you new here?'

'Yes, I'm Mairi', she said.

40.   Payline
by Heather Marshall

Charlie sits, hunched, on a bench between the arcade and the pebbled shore. Behind him, a gaggle of girls giggles out, their pitch in harmony with the tinkly music and sounds of one-armed bandits in play. Coins roll down the insides of the machines, become losers' money. Charlie knows the fleeting thrill of the play, the pull on the arm, the delight as the columns whirl with hope, suspended overhead. He knows the clenching of the gut as the columns lower, lower, lower, then settle, one-two-three. If the game is lost, the player must decide if the risk is worth playing again.

Charlie glances up the street, inland. He shifts his feet inside his black leather shoes. Does his jacket hide the coffee stain on his shirt? Grey-blue to match his eyes, Yves St. Laurent.

Largs is packed. It was the same on Cumbrae as he made his way to the ferry – loud children stuffing in ice creams, washing them down with Irn Brus. Charlie can't fathom why it's like this on a Monday, but then Charlie has never known the rhythm of children, the sway of school holidays. He thinks of this as he looks south down the firth; he thinks these swarms of children will make the woman he's waiting for harder to spot. They also camouflage him.

Charlie wants to see her first no matter which way she comes – along the front towards him, from the ferry, from the top of the village; even if she comes from behind the arcade, she will have to cross the street in front of him. Grace. Her name whirls in his head. He has not yet tested it on his lips, felt it rise from his throat, vibrating, filling his mouth, then floating out from him into the world. This is what Grace did: came from him, unbidden, unknown, before she was taken away.

He'd thought it would be himself who would be away, forty-one years ago, when he came across the water and up the firth and in along the Clyde to Glasgow. He earned good marks in his course, gathered a girl by his side. The pair of them drank pints of heavy in the pubs, pointed to places on the map of the world that they might go when she was a fully qualified nurse and he an engineer. Less than a year it took them, to land in separate places, their baby settling with a couple on the other side of the country. Later, he landed a job at Hunterston, on the mainland, at least.

Even that is finished now, and himself tucked back in to his dead parents' house whilst his daughter has been out in the world, away over Cumbrae and all Scotland's westernmost isles, right on to America, so her letter said. He's never known where her mother went.

He straightens his spine, there on the bench.

Any moment now, Grace will complete her journey back to him.

The village surges. Charlie's belly rolls. His heart thumps. When was he last this aware? His skin tingles. Charlie presses his hands on his thighs, pulls in his belly.

He recalls his own father, decades ago, outside the arcade, a special Saturday when they'd gone the opposite direction of the Glaswegians. He recalls his father's callused fingers pressing coins into Charlie's small, smooth-skinned hand. He recalls the cigarette-rough of the old man's voice, saying, "That's all you get."

"Hold your winnings," he said. "Only fools go in again."

Charlie could rise now, slip away. He smoothes his trousers, presses back his shoulders.

He sees her, striding down from the top of the village, auburn hair flowing behind her like a wake. The village stills. Everything falls away – the girls giggling, the ferry churning, the slot machines twirling.

Charlie watches her pass on the opposite side of the street, stands to move to her, the moment suspended. *Grace.*

Charlie steps across the street. Grace has stopped. She turns.

Charlie stops, inches from her, this girl, this woman, his daughter.

"Grace." Charlie leans, hand extended, waiting for her hand to land in his.

other islands

41. Kaolin
by Heather Marshall

Late autumn, just beyond the peak of hurricane season, she tells him she wants to go to Sesay. He watches as she loads her tools into the skiff, which she insists they take, shunning not only the small ferry to the new, gated club at the north end of the island, but also the public one, which she took as a child. She insists on being the one who rows, pulling away from the mainland, facing what she's leaving. The waters are calm, a clear sky and bright fall sun overhead. She keeps her eyes bare while he shelters behind his Ray Bans.

On Sesay, named for the tribe of one of the first freed slaves to live there, she pulls the boat clear of the high tide mark before he has the chance to get the gear out. She lifts her bucket, strides on, leaving him to grab the tent and backpack and follow her down a skinny, sandy path. Here there are neither boardwalks nor tourists to clatter across them. The sun is filtered first by Palmetto trees, then pine, then cypress. Ahead, her kinky blonde hair, corralled into a ponytail, bounces to her internal rhythm. When they reach what he imagines must be the heart of the island, out of reach of brackish water, she stops on the trail, points to a clearing at the edge of still, dark waters. There's room for the tent and not much else.

"Are you sure it isn't tidal?" he asks.

She isn't.

His back against the bark, he drives in a stake between the knees of a cypress anyway. The dark limbs of the trees disappear into the swamp on the other side of him.

On her haunches at the edge, she runs her hand under the tannin-stained waters, lifting fingers again and again. In the sunlight, the drops become clear against her skin, cling to the ends of the delicate blond hairs on her arms. She slips off her loose trousers, baggy t-shirt, silky underthings; she slides in, white neck and face above. Her body becomes part of the dark below.

Suspended in the water, she digs fingers into pale kaolinite. This is what they have come for, to dig out and take home some of this most important class of rock-forming materials. She has explained to him about this clay, a layered silicate, almost the precise shade of her own skin; she whispered to him about the secret shape of it, the tetrahedral sheet using oxygen atoms to bind to the sheet of alumina octahedra.

"It's like working in air and earth at the same time," she had said.

She rubs a little onto her face, breathes deeply. He watches, there on the bank, tent stake in hand, as she binds herself in earth and air and water, elemental.

He recalls her telling of her grandmother, raised on the island. Octoroon, one-eighth black, the granddaughter of freed slaves, she was pale enough to pass for white. At eighteen, she rowed herself off Sesay, walked inland and north; she left her family, changed her clothes and her name along the way. Wanga, meaning charm, wouldn't serve her in her new life as a white woman. She passed easily; she met a white man that first week in New York, married him some months later. She became pregnant, then afraid.

"She got scared of giving him a baby with kinky-coily hair, the cocoa skin of her own grandmother. She told him. He paid her ticket back to Savannah."

She walked twenty miles to the dock, found a boat that looked like hers, took back her name, rowed herself home. A honey-colored baby came some months later, with a thick head of blonde hair, kinky as she'd feared, the same kind of kinky hair he watches in the next generation.

He recalls her telling of weekends on Sesay, Wanga taking her digging for oysters. They ate a few, raw. They roasted a few more over the pit, never getting full because they had to sell enough to pay the tax man, to keep hold of their land. The whole island had been deemed worthless, good enough only for freed slaves after the Civil War; it stayed that way until air conditioning brought white folks down. Island paradise, dotted just a few minutes powerboat ride from the Carolina coast. The land became valuable, then; the taxes increased.

He watches her now, dig into the soft clay; he recalls her telling of Wanga's hands, raw and red, risking the gash of the shell to save her little bit of ground.

His own family came from an island 3,000 miles east and north of hers. His father, born there but not much more, took him once. They boarded the plane and then the train and then took a ferry across the Firth of Clyde to what, in his teenaged estimation, wasn't much more than a whale-hump of land. He hired a bicycle, rode it around the island like the rest of the tourists. Fifty-two minutes, it took him. His legs ached for a greater distance. In the evenings, in the one pub with his father and grandfather and the few men still resident – a handful of farmers and fishers, a priest and a publican – he felt he couldn't get a whole chestful of air. Perhaps it was just the smoke, as his father said.

By the end of the week, he had to hold in the impulse to sprint to the ferry. He paced on the train, sat awake on the plane. At home, he packed his bicycle, rode 120 miles in one direction in a day. He hadn't even reached the top of the state. In his tent that night, he lay on his back,

214

hands clasped on his chest, thought of the whole broad continent. He slept immediately, finding a peace he might have thought reserved only for the dead.

He still has that tent, reserved for solo trips; the tent he stakes down on Sesay is two generations beyond. He spreads the cover in front of it, spreads himself on top of it, watching her.

When she has gathered all she wants, he lifts her, dripping, clay spattered – earth and water, blood and bone. They slide onto the tent cover, still spread on the ground; they don't care that they are leaving the dug clay exposed, that the cover will be hell to clean. Afterwards, they wrap the clay, rinse in swamp water, forget about covering the tent.   In the morning, they shake off the dried shards, turn for home.

"What will it be this time?" He asks this as they break camp.

She raises eyebrows, early light drawing the tinge of fire in them. "Patience." Like a girl making a boy wait until the next date, and the next, and the next. But she has always shown him.

He has seen nothing of it by early winter, when he finds himself deep in the city. He thinks of it, standing at her side in a white room at the end of a linoleum corridor. They listen as the doctor tells them he has dug out the mass, found it black and sprawling underneath the surface.

"Like cypress," she burbles, still half under the anesthesia. "Take me."

He dismisses the request as the talk of the anesthesia. He wheels her back down the hall, into the stainless steel elevator. In the lobby, he rolls her past the player piano that tinkles across from the fountain, the eternally plump renaissance boy in the center.

Outside, under a weak sun, she presses out of the wheelchair before he can steady her. She wobbles, extends her left hand, palm out, saying, *Stop!* or, *Stay back!* wordless. She eases to a squat, presses palms to ground, turns her face to the sky.

"Take me," she says.

When the stitches are removed, he drives her, then rows, he thinks for the day, back to the place beyond the brackish water so she can feel her hands in yielding earth. Hadn't she told him it helps form 90% of the earth's crust?

He watches her, in chilled air, strip, goosebumps rising before she slides slowly in, fingers clutching the clay bank. To stop himself from rushing forward, helping her when she doesn't want it, he recites, in his head, what he can remember. He thinks of her as the kaolinite itself, formed from chemical weathering, undergoing transformations made through heat in air at atmospheric pressure. He thinks of her as porcelain, fired at over 1,200 C. He recalls her voice:

The Chinese wrote that the kaolin formed the bones of the paste; the refined rocks were the flesh.

Her triceps quiver as she tries to push herself up and out. He steps forward. "Tony." She grimaces. He steps back.

"I need to be here," she says.

He recalls her telling him she felt uneasy moving in when Wanga passed, and left the house to her. She kept her home on the mainland, checked on Wanga's house occasionally. She thought herself too pale to live on Sesay. Weren't there enough white people molesting the island? Now, on this, the free side of the gate, she wants to stake her claim.

She sends him for gear. She sends him for supplies. When he returns, he finds her, paler than clay, hammer in hand, shoring up Wanga's walls. He takes the ferry in the mornings, to work on the mainland, and at sunset, back; she insists on rowing herself, once a week, for treatment. She paints the walls, repairs the porch; hurricane season is long past.

January brings a rare frost. The same week, she asks him to row her. She refuses to return to live on the mainland.

He is still rowing her, twice a week now, in March. Mid-month, he wakes, facing the window. *Birds,* he thinks first. *Soon she can sit on the porch, wrapped in one less blanket. She can watch the earth unravel again.* He recalls her smile, broad, taking her whole face.

The English thought they meant real bone. There's a recipe. Two parts bone ash, one part kaolin clay, one part china stone.

He rolls over, finds her breath thready. He presses his fingertips to the edge of her throat, the way the nurse showed him. He does not need to check her blood pressure.

Before they arrive, he lifts her. Spring light filters through curtains in the hallway as he carries her again, outside. Her eyelids flutter but do not open as he presses her hand against the earth. He waits there, wonders only briefly if she'd want him to shun the water ambulance from the gated section; he slips her onto the gurney, just beyond dawn.

It will be summer, the start of hurricane season, before he forces himself to the skiff again, to the sandy path. He will find, in the out-building, beside the oyster buckets, her kaolinite likeness, a self-portrait in three dimensions, shiny silicate clinging to oxygen, unfinished, hairless. He will lift her, this one last, unexpected time. He will recall her telling him her name meant wearer of the mask in Africa. Before that, he'd known only the Greek derivation – life.

He will wonder, as he carries her likeness, wrapped carefully, to the spot, would she want him to stay? He will carry the jar containing her ashes, too. He will sit, as she did, on haunches, hold the smooth lump of her in one hand, close his eyes, trace her one last time – her eyes, lazy-lidded as they were, after, in the tent, the perfect curve of nose, lips slightly parted. He will recall that teenage visit to his father's island, his restless circuits around the circumference. What might he have uncovered had he been able to rest in the heart of the land and dig down?

He will hesitate, his finger on her lips. He will plunge into the kaolin. There at the edge, he will mix the ashes of her, bone and flesh, with this most important silicate. He will press and pull until they are one. He will pull her to him, breathe her in one last time, whisper her name – *Zoe* – before he slips them under.

42. On the Bikini Atoll
by Thomas Rist

They are complaining now
those old men
with cancers, deformities

saying they should have had masks
or suits or boots
or that they shouldn't have been there at all

and then you see
these soldiers, line upon line,
looking to sea

where the bomb will destroy
atoms and dust and even
order, reason in nature,

so that their uniform
turn of command,
their military symmetry
giving their backs to the sea
like a wilful blindness,
looks like nostalgia.
Not that I'm not

sympathetic or wouldn't
uphold the old men,

not that I don't think
everything they can be given
they should be given

or that their cries
shouldn't be heard
as if by nurses,

no. Who give all
deserve all, like these men,
though few give as much

and who wouldn't turn away
at the sentence of death
when a word like cancer

explodes with a noise you can't hear?

In 1946, nuclear tests were conducted on the Bikini Atoll in the Pacific.

43. His Island Life
by Natasha Yapp

You are
A Father of sorts with
A soft paternal mouth with
A mouthful of guilt and childhood sores and
Eyes of apologetic abandonment and
I misunderstand your reasoning but
I love you like a faithful daughter should and
What does it matter because
A looming illness silences all indiscretions.

Malaysia, all reds and greens
Patriarchal Proboscis observes atop the trees
Heat like a sauna, moisture like a steam room
Sun-kissed in the tropics
Sweat pores hollow awkward topics
Sunstroke in your mind
A beautiful aneurysm
Suffocating the memories I never had
I dream in heat
I recall no ideal Father, man.

Talking becomes, somehow, malapropos
Lu cha and bubble tea leaves
A mosquito sang bitterly in my ears,
It bit me in my sleep anaesthetically

Ugly cockroaches run ragged across the floor.

We breakfast together, happily when
I suck on fat and salt like an antidote
I choke on chicken feet throughout bonding I
Wolf plate after plate of *dim sum* as though each mouthful
Makes up for lost time, lost culture.
I hear Chinese chatter
I hear Chinese laughter
But I don't understand what is said.

Vermin
Orange brick and a house
Of ants, cockroaches, psychedelic bugs
Of inertia, insects in every corner,
We are three, buzzing TV
We feast by the drains and I watch every step.

Laughing is delightful in theory -
We have a different vocabulary for the past,
We share the same mother tongue, but yours
Your father tongue
With a foreign accent
One which I delight in hearing at Christmas.

44. The Photograph
by Charlotte Johnson

My chair fills the bay window. Sitting here, I can follow the weather travelling across the loch: it changes minute by minute. Rainstorms sweep in from the Atlantic, dark clouds dumping their cargo of water like sea-planes fighting fires. Today there are no clouds; the sea is flat, glass-like, reflecting houses and boats as though they are sitting on a mirror. The tide is low and people on the small beach are enjoying the warm sun.

I watch a small girl digging. Full of energy, she scoops sand on to her spade and throws it into the bucket, spadeful after spadeful, half of it flying through the air to land on the legs of a woman, lying on a rug, beside her. Half-heartedly, languidly, she reaches her arm down to brush away the sand and lifting the brim of her hat peeks out from under it to say something to the man beside her.

He shrugs, gets up, and stretches his tall, lean frame before dropping down on his hunkers beside the toddler. They go through the time-honoured ritual of patting the sand firmly into the patterned bucket and taking her hands he places them on the edge of the bucket's rim. Together they turn it upside down on to the sand. He mimics hitting the top of the bucket with the spade. She copies him.

Tap one, tap two, tap three.

'Abracadabra' I whisper as he lifts the bucket to reveal the turrets of the sandcastle she has made. She jumps up and down, clapping in excitement. Laughing, the man swings her up into the air. Dancing, whirling, spinning, their joy written on their faces as slowing down, he gently lowers her beside their work of art.

I stand on a beach with my own father. Such a clear image: I can see the colour of my swimsuit, goldie-yellow, elasticated and ruched, it looks like little bubbles. My mother loved it because it was nylon and dried quickly. I loathed it. It bulged at the front and back as I got out of the water, filling up like a buoy. I looked like I had a potbelly and a sagging bottom. Where was the beach? Donegal? A trip to Inishfree? Somewhere there is a picture of us paddling.

I rummage through boxes of photographs to find the one marked 'Childhood'. There aren't so many in this box; we didn't own a camera nor did my parents set much store to capturing our lives on film. The few photos I have were taken by relatives and family friends.

I pull out one of us standing in front of a car. I'm probably about nine years old. The black and white picture is crumpled, faded around the edges. My father, smiling, leans against a car bonnet, holding my hand. My mother stands on the other side of me, holding her handbag. She wears a patterned summer dress and sunglasses. I remember her dress and fill in the colours – white background with pretty pink, red and yellow roses. I am wearing my 'tomboy' uniform of shorts and tee shirt, my long hair in plaits with ribbons - my mother's finishing touch, her silent appeal to me at the beginning of each day to be more feminine. We look like a model family - happy in the sunshine.

I'm pretty sure this was taken on the same holiday.

We had stayed with my Aunt Jane and Uncle Sandy. Or, as my father put it: 'Staying with the minister and his good wife, in the back of beyond.'

'Shush, Johnny' My mother smiled, nudging him. My father had the knack of saying the things other people thought and were too polite to say. It got him into hot water with her on more than one occasion.

Uncle Sandy and his family lived near Cresslough, a small seaside town in Donegal. My cousin, Anne, hated living there, she held the same opinion as my father but put it more strongly: 'No, the back of beyond is somewhere. This is the end of the road to nowhere'. She left home as soon as she could for the bright lights of Belfast.

I look at the picture again. I remember the car – my father's pride and joy, a light blue Daimler with plump red leather seats and walnut trim on the dashboard.

'Beautiful wood, walnut, lovely patterns' he'd say as he polished the trim. I was never quite sure who he was talking to - me or himself. That year there was a turquoise paper triangle on the windscreen - the permit you needed to cross the border from Northern Ireland into the Free State. Driving through the checkpoint on the Ulster side across a short strip of road to another country was exciting. We were going somewhere 'foreign' but not across the water. The Garda would come out from their border post to check your papers and the stamp on the triangle; if you didn't have one or it wasn't the right colour, you were sent back.

We'd driven from Belfast to Donegal for a week's holiday. This was unusual, in fact, this is the only time I can remember him taking more than a few days off. It sticks in my memory because it was our last holiday together.

A week together - a big event for the two families – filled with excursions to different beaches and once, a meal in the hotel at Marble Hill. I protest when my mother insists I wear the dress she had packed for a special occasion. But my excitement at high tea in a hotel won out against her threat that I wouldn't be going at all if I didn't put it on. The dreaded frock was worn: the fish and chips with bread and butter, followed by an ice-cream sundae was well worth the teasing my cousins gave me.

The best day of the holiday is our trip to the small island of Inishfree.
'I will arise and go now, and go to Inisfree....', my father recited, winking at me in the driver's mirror. 'Well, we're arising and going, aren't we? And what will we find there: a small cabin, nine bean rows and a hive for the honey bee? But of course, it's not his Inisfree we're going to, is it Lizzie?' My mother didn't answer, concentrating on her crossword. 'That's an island on a lough, not a wee

island in the Atlantic. Still, it's a pretty poem. 'And I shall have some peace there, for peace comes dropping slow, Dropping from the vales of morning to where the cricket sings…' his voice tailed off. 'Ah, peace, we could all do with some of that, couldn't we? Do you think the Provos and Loyalists learnt WB Yeats when they were at school? Much good it's done any of them.' Tutting, he shook his head. I heard his dismay, but didn't know until much later that he'd had trouble with both groups. He was a fair man and prided himself on employing the best man for the job. 'Protestant, Catholic, Hindu, what does it matter as long as they can do the work I pay them for?' They kill and maim innocent folk in the name of the very people struggling to put hand to mouth because of their violence. 'Put them in a room together, lock the door and let them get on with it'.

He had no patience with the views or tactics of either group. What would he have thought if he'd lived longer through the mayhem that was coming our way.

At Burtonport we take the ferry to Inishfree. A seal bobs up to say hello as we make the crossing to the island's harbour. Then, we pile off the boat and trek across silver white sand, so fine it trickles immediately to cover our footprints. There are sand bars out in the distance, water glistening like diamonds. We walk until the grown-ups agree on a place to stop with shelter from the breeze, space to play in the sand and a good place to swim.

We settle ourselves, putting up windbreakers, laying out the rugs and towels. The women sort out food, getting ready for the picnic. The men thump the windbreakers down into the sand with a mallet and, we, the children, change into our swimsuits. The hard bit about this ritual is putting on your costume without half the beach ending up inside it.

When we have changed, we go to find a patch of harder sand and put up the cricket stumps ready for the big game. It's always a 'big game' when we're together; 'Strive to Win' could be the family motto. I wander off with my bucket and spade. As the youngest I'll be the last one picked. This doesn't worry me; I'm happy playing alone in the softer sand.

We're called for lunch and, for a while, there is relative quiet as we chew our way through tinned salmon (the height of sophistication for picnics) and beef paste sandwiches. There are boiled eggs, which I hate, and Aunt Jane's famous chocolate and orange cake which I love. There is a thermos of tea for the grownups and pop for the children. By the time we're finished, everyone is laughing - food always puts our family in a good mood.

The women clear up the debris from lunch and the men lie around reading the papers. Told to rest before playing cricket, we disperse in small groups. The boys practise their bowling and the girls sit and chatter about what pop groups they like (the Beatles, of course) and who they want to sit beside when they go back to school.

I hang around on the edge of the conversation and try to tell Pat and Anne about my friend, Karen, who went to see the Beatles in Belfast.

'You're making it up,' Pat says. 'What nine-year old goes to see the Beatles?' She raises her eyebrows and Anne laughs.

'But, it's true, she did,' I kick at the sand with my foot, not quite hard enough for it to hit her. She hisses, moving her legs, 'Go away, baby.'

'It's true, she did so. She did go and see them and you're just jealous.' I stick my tongue out and run through the sand spraying golden rivulets down on to her legs. Pat shrieks.

'I hate her,' the thought runs with me down to the sea, my own jealousy at Karen's Beatles adventure vanishing with each step.

There are all sorts of shells lying above the tide-line so I decide to get my bucket again; I'll make a sandcastle and decorate it with shells I collect. The boys are shouting, egging each other on about their bowling skills, or lack of them. They're ready for the game and pester the grownups to come and join in.

My dad gets up and comes towards me, 'Come on, Isabel Necessary on a Bicycle', we'll go and collect some shells'. He nods to the boys, 'You don't need us, we'll go for a walk.' My mum waves without looking; she is busy with another crossword and isn't bothered about cricket or walks, just the next clue.

We walk down the beach to the water's edge. Dad lights up a cigarette. He blows silvery-grey smoke into the air. He is quiet, like he's savouring the experience. He flicks the cigarette end on the beach and kicks sand over it. We walk a bit further. He stops, 'Wait a minute,' he sits down and rolls his trousers up to his knees. I'm surprised by his white legs and feet, his face and hands are brown.

He gets up, stretching out his hand, 'Come on then, let's have a paddle.'

His hand is warm and strong. We walk to where the small waves are coming in and the first one hits our feet, 'Brrr, it's cold,' he shouts, laughing as he splashes in up to his ankles. He hops from one foot to the other and grins at me: a big wide, mischievous grin. He kicks and an arc of silver rises from his toes: I'm transfixed by a rainbow shining in the air before ice drops down on to my arms and legs. I scream at the coldness on my warm skin and run away. He kicks another arc and we make our way along the beach this way; I run away as he sees how far he can kick the water and if it will reach me. We laugh and laugh: it doesn't matter that we're wet. It's fun. He was fun.

He stops and points, 'Look, seals on the sandbar.' On a flat patch of sand further out on the water, a group of seals bask in the sun. He points again, 'Well, will you look at that,' his voice filled with surprise. 'See, over in the trees, at the other side of the beach.'

I look, and there in the dappled shade of the trees is a grey building. At one side, near to the trees, four men play tennis. They are monks, dressed in long white robes, hitting the ball across the net and running about the court. We hear laughter carrying across the water. The thwack of a ball against a racquet. Somehow they manage to look as if playing tennis in monks' garb is the most natural thing in the world.

'I'll be blowed,' he says laughing, "I thought I'd seen everything …'

The phone rings. I answer slowly.

'Mum, what are you doing?' Jennie asks.

'Remembering – an island, your granddad'.

'Right,' she races on, 'Tell me in a few minutes, I'm on my way over. Put the kettle on, I'm absolutely parched.'

I carefully replace the photo of us standing by the car into my box. It is all I have left of him, after all. The memory is clear, focussed; I feel I've been back on the beach on that small island with my father.

I walk into the kitchen.
'I will arise and go now and go to Inisfree', I recite as Jennie clatters into the hallway.

45. Stranded
by Morag Henriksen

You know how on a summer's day
the headland's bright
with sunshine
and the sound beyond is blue.
You want to sail out to the island
over there.

You know you have the knowledge
and the skills,
the boat, the engine
then
white fog rolls inland from the sea
and dims the edges,
wraps it about in cottonwool,
obscures the landfalls,
blocks the way
with stuff you cannot get a grip on.

You are powerless.
Stuck.
You have the wish,
the urge,
the knowledge and desire
and yet you cannot reach your island.

That's what it's like
to have M.E.
Fog banks roll in,
obliterate your mind
and leave you at a standstill.

history

46. The Meeting
by Liz Shaw

Love and Music Will Endure: A novel based on the life of Màiri Mhòr nan Òran

Chapter 1: The Meeting
Skeabost House, the Isle of Skye, 1891.

Is it the fox? Is it about the fox's stink? she wondered. She knew that the neighbours would have been complaining to him about it, grumbles sneaking out of the corners of their mouths. She strained to follow the scent. Why had the summons come now? Her mind scavenged for clues. She jabbed the tip of her umbrella between the stones as she strode along the driveway sweeping beside the river towards the loch.

'Walk tall, like Finn McCoul. Pound the earth beneath your feet.' That's what Pappa would say.

Well I've done that often enough and enjoyed seeing my enemies tremble but it's hard to keep roaring now I'm old and battle scarred, she imagined replying to him. He had only known her when she was young with a high tide surging through her. How her Mamma used to shake her head at that strong current, the vigour within her that flooded over the banks of womanly behaviour.

'You've been trouble right from the start. What a hard time I had bringing you into the world. You had to be contrary even then, ripping your way out backwards. And then you were always famished and suckled like a ravening beast.'

She stopped to catch her breath, looking down to check her shoes for mud. Those wretched corsets, nipping her as she bent. She lifted each of her heavy men's brogues in turn, grunting with the effort and scrubbed them through a clump of grass. When she was a child her mother had complained about how fast she grew. Màiri felt like a bumbling giant as she snagged her skirt on brambles or her raw boned frame burst the seams of her blouse yet again. To Mamma she was a boisterous heifer erupting from the winter byre with green meadow memories in her nostrils and trampling everything in her path.

There was the big house looming ahead, still looking raw and new laid against the dun coloured, muted winter landscape. The tower stabbed upwards, a thick accusing finger. What was she to be accused of? As a young woman when blame had struck her like a lightning bolt she had tried to flow quietly and not let the torrents spill over. But what use had meekness been when she had to fend for herself later on? Frowning she turned down the side wall leading to the back of the house. She kicked a loose stone, skidding it down the slope. Then she hauled out a glowing white handkerchief to swab her dripping face before heading towards the back entrance, the one used by servants, tradesmen and tenants. She had waited often enough at similar doors with Pappa when he came to pay his rent. Most of the men would shuffle in when it was their turn, caps crushed in their hands. A few sauntered in, hands plunged in pockets. Most commented on the weather, some enquired after the landlord's health, others ventured a joke. All of them though, bar one or two who were ostentatiously pious, accepted a dram, smacking their lips as the welcome heat slid down their throats. What did Pappa do? He held himself as steady as the Old Man of Storr himself and then marched in with dignity – a nod but no smile.

'I'm not a supplicant,' He would say. And neither was she. All those years she had spent on platforms, the audience tight-packed as seabirds on a cliff, their cheers swirling around her. Had it been a mistake to return home? It was true that a prophet was without honour in his own land. She had done the neighbourly thing – calling on folk with a basket of warm bannocks on her arm. But people had changed their ways. They didn't want to be shown how to spin a strong woollen thread or how to cook herring the old way, straight on the peats. The lairds and their ladies were welcoming enough but they expected her to sing for her supper. Was that all she was now - an entertaining character? What about everything she had fought for? The Land League was fading from people's memories as if it had never been - just like the mighty Cuillin itself could be so smothered in mist that it disappeared from sight. We're all old now, our fine, fresh hopes curdled, she thought.

Taking a deep breath she swayed, broad-beamed, around the corner, the wind plucking at the edges of her plaid cape, billowing it behind her. She looked over the calm sweep of Loch Snizort. The wind twitched the shimmering water, creasing its satin surface and splashing beads of rainbow light. She sucked in the moist air and let her lips stretch into a smile. The land was constant; it would always succour her. She had lived through terrors - the night-time thud on the door, the rough grasp on her arm, the shame of the prison cell. After all of that she could surely face up to a disapproving landlord?

She looked back towards the house and suddenly she realised that she could see right in through the window. She sidled closer. There was a small table there holding a brass tray. Shiny enough but it would be the better for more elbow grease. She could make out strange, curved figures carved on it. He must have brought it back from India. What were they? Beasts of some kind? No – the legs surely belonged to people. Some sort of heathen gods? But four legs tangled together- surely not? They wouldn't show that – a man and a woman coupled together? She chuckled out loud. Then with a jolt she sawMr Macdonald himself heading towards the window. She stayed stock still, hardly daring to breathe. His fine, thin, face looked stern, his lips pressed together but – thank goodness – he was looking down at the table, not out of the window. His fingers reached out to a decanter and then leapt back as if they had been burnt. Stiffly he walked back to a chair and sat down, putting his face in his hands. Now her own hands were shaking so much that she had to squeeze them together. He must be brooding about how he would tell her to leave. Had Donald Stewart come to moan about what she had said to him the week before?

'I won't make a song to a man unless he's worthy.

Although I get a hundred dresses on my doorstep.'

I'll stand by that, she thought. The man had no right to take advantage just because of who I am. But no doubt he whispered poison inMr MacDonald's ear. Did he pay attention to it?

Where would she rest her head if she was turned out? Her children were scattered seed and her old friend

Margaret back to Australia. Plenty would say that it served her right for getting above herself. Widows are expected to stay at home, Bible and knitting to hand. 'Crowing hens and whistling women are an abomination to the Lord,' as Mamma would say.

She wandered nearer to the shore and willed the calm water to flow through her. I won't leave the island I love for a second time she vowed as she tramped up to the door and knocked hard. She could hear shuffling before it was opened. It was himself, adjusting a frown into a smile.

'Welcome, Mistress MacPherson. Will you not come in?'

He levered himself into a chair. Her nervous eyes flickered around the room, quick as a fox's snout.

'You've not been in the estate office before? I was just finishing looking over some papers but I confess I expected you to use the front entrance, as before.'

'But you wanted to see me about the cottage – that's why I came round the back. The fox has run off you know. I've no man to share my life and now not even a male animal. I don't know what Mr Stewart has said….'

She blundered on but staggered to a halt when she saw how baffled he looked.

'I don't understand what your house – or indeedMr Stewart - has to do with our meeting. The house is yours for as long as you want it.'

She made a sort of sobbing laugh and stifled it in her handkerchief. 'And I'm grateful although there are Land Leaguers who still condemn me for accepting it.'

'They think that you fawn on the gentry?'

She snorted. 'They wanted me at the big meetings on Skye but did any of them offer me a roof over my head?' She gave him an appraising look. 'Do you know that during all those years of the troubles you were the only landlord who could go about in a pony and trap?'

He looked puzzled. 'All the others had to ride in a closed carriage for fear of having mud, stones or worse thrown at them,' she whooped, slapping her thigh.

'I'm relieved no-one disliked me enough to hurl the likes at me. Now if you'll excuse me for a moment.'

He stood up and limped to the door.

What a silly *cailleach* he must think me, blethering on about the fox. So why did he summon me?

He came back, a boyish grin on his face and his hands clasped behind his back. Then he thrust one arm forward. 'I wanted you to see this.' His hand cradled something small, oblong and vividly red.

She took it, bracing her arms as if it was heavy. She squinted at it and turned it over before pressing it against her cheek. What did it smell of? Did it smell of a warm cow's flank or of a crisp winter's day that turned your breath to trails of smoke? It should smell of the countryside that had made it. Mamma used to say how parched she used to feel when they stayed in Glasgow, longing to gulp down Highland air.

'Do open it,' he coaxed.

She sighed and nestled it tenderly on her lap. Her fingers rummaged inside the bodice of her best dark purple gown, stumbling over the tiny buttons. He looked a little alarmed but smiled when he saw her pulling out a pearl handled magnifying glass. Her eyes were too misted to fix on the bird tracks of the letters.

'I can't take it in. These were all stored away in my head for so long and now they're here. It was like waiting for my children to be born. I wondered what each of them would be like but I still couldn't believe it when a new stranger appeared.'

He nodded.

'Yet birth reminds me of death too. One of my daughters died young.'

He shuddered. 'Do you like the printing?'

'So many words – it took me so long to sing them all. I don't know how I managed it.'

'Well, if you recollectMr White travelled up from Inverness and spent many hours writing them down at your dictation.'

'I can write a fair English hand but I never learnt to write Gaelic properly. I wouldn't want scholars to find mistakes.' She was pleased to see that he looked a little uncomfortable at her reproach.

'No, indeed. What do you think of the photographs of you preparing the tweed?'

She decided to be gracious. 'Very good. Of course I was brought up to learn all the household skills - not like young women today who expect to buy everything from shops.' She sniffed.

'There'll be a more formal presentation later but I thought you should see it first, hot from the press. It's a record of all those words that inspired your fellow Highlanders fighting for justice.'

'It's good that no-one can be thrown off the land anymore and have their homes torn down around them. But there are still so many hungry for land. I used to imagine that the wheel would turn and bring back the descendants of the folk driven from the island. I believed that the *Bugha Mòr* would ring again to children's voices and the shouts of young men playing shinty.'

A silence fell between them. He broke it first.

'Whatever the rights and wrongs of the Land Wars, the publication of your poetry is a cause for celebration. When my tenants come in here I offer them a wee dram although I know the minister disapproves. Perhaps a glass of wine would be more suitable today.'

She laughed. 'No, I'm happy to take a dram. It warms the heart and belly much better than your thin foreign stuff.'

'You don't adhere to the temperance rules, then?' he said with a grin as he struggled to his feet and hobbled over to the table. 'Forgive me for toasting you with water. This wretched gout is plaguing me at the moment.'

'I've always followed the Church's teachings, especially about keeping the Sabbath day holy. But I'll never understand how folk can be so peculiar that gloom becomes the food they eat. Song, shinty and the water of life all bring joy to our lives'.

'I couldn't agree with you more. I propose a toast to the success of your book and to all of us exiles returned to our native island'.

She downed her drink in one swallow and sighed in appreciation. He half rose from his seat as if he was about to usher her out. Not so quickly, she thought. After all, his summons had caused her all that worry which was not good for a woman of her years. It was time for her to call the tune. She tapped the cover of the book.

'Before I go we should sing one of my songs. What about, "Farewell to the Island of Mists"?'

'Well – There're a lot of verses and my voice is rather scratchy these days.'

'Seventeen in total, I believe. I have them by heart but you may borrow the wee book of words if you wish,' she said, digging him in the ribs with an elbow.

He knew when he was beaten. So they sang together in Gaelic. His voice was true if a little croaky, she thought. She wished that he wouldn't sing with his hands in his pockets as so many men did. They stood side by side looking out at the loch held in the folds of the low hills. Sky and water seeped and smudged together, like colours painted on silk.

'Farewell to the place I grew up
To the mountains topped with clouds
Rose coloured skies of morning
Sweeping out of the darkness
Lighting up the Storr.
Sights more beautiful the eye could never see
Cattle out grazing on a peaceful sunny morning
The lark on the wing singing confidently her music
The mist surrounding Beinn Tianabhaig
And the mountain under dew.'

47. Gernemwa, 1238
i.m. Alexina NicCoinnich
by Peter MacKay

Bhog iad an sgadan ann am mear-shalann 's creag-shalann
's ghrèidh iad os cionn darag 's caorain iad,
an fheòil a' dol dearg tron oidhche
mar gum b' ann am braonan-fraoich no màdar-fraoich

's tha iad a' cumail a' chiad leth-cheud baraill,
mar bu dual dhaibh, dhaibh fhèin,
an còrr aig oir a' chala mar bhalla
a' feitheamh air na fir on Tuath

a bheir leotha am Frìoslais 's an sgeulachdan
de thallan fuilteach 's sheòid nan Geota
's a dh'fhàgas às an dèidh cnapan òmair,
's snaidhmean a dh'fhosglas sa bhrù.

Gun fhios dhaibh tha na Tartaran a' tighinn
le an èiginn 's an losgadh 's an creach:
grodaidh na h-èisg ann an ataireachd an t-samhraidh,
drùidhidh an fhèoil troimhe gu gine na cloiche,

creicidh iad baraill 's baraill 'son pòran
is na stòpanan deoch-meala 's leann
leis an òlte deoch-shlàinte dhan sgadan
is do lainnir nan lannan sna tuinn.

Gernemwa: seann ainm air Great Yarmouth

Gernemwa, 1238
i.m. Alexina Mackenzie
Peter MacKay

They soaked the herring in brine and saltpetre,
smoked them over oak and turf fires,
the flesh dying red overnight
as if in tormentil or ladies' bedstraw

and they have kept the first ton of butts
for themselves as is their custom;
the rest are stacked as a wall in the harbour
awaiting the men from the North

who'll bring with them their Friesian and stories
of bloodied halls and the heroes of Götts,
leave behind them nuggets of amber,
and knots that will open in wombs.

They don't know the Tartars are coming
with their burning and pillage and rape;
the fish will rot in the swelling of summer,
stain through to the grain in the stone,

and they'll swap barrel on barrel for cornseed
for the flagons of porter and mead

that toasted the return of the herring,
and the gleam of their scales in the sea.

Gernemwa: an old name for Great Yarmouth

48. Fàgail
by Andy Jackson

He is the last of all to leave this place,
waiting for the Admiralty sloop, a refugee
pursued by no-one. Hands like claws
and scabrous skin the pallor of the sea,
he wears the North Atlantic on his face.

His home is ceded to the slew of gulls,
immutable chaos of beak and feather,
the only real government here. The fall
of man approaches, low pressure
roaring in, a revolutionary squall.

Throughout inconstancies of weather
he has clung like topsoil to the fact
of this isle, but, as would a doomed lover,
it now pushes him away, a wordless act
of kindness, knowing it is over.

The final parliament dissolved, the vote
not carried, it is time to face the sea
again and set adrift the seaborne note
that says that you were here, that *we*
were here. Now, step onto the boat.

49. The Ship
by John Maguire

I could have sat here by the bothy
as the cool May evening starts to fade,
one hundred and fifty years ago,
and looked down over the low stone walls,
the fields with the broken cross, and crows
restless among the grazing sheep,
to see this ship, three-masted, ghosting
under full sail between the hills
of Rum and Canna: a great white moth
drawn towards the westering sun.

lasting effect of the island

50. Fugitive
by Ruth Aylett

When you came to the island first,
Its boundaries seemed safe and
Those long treeless vistas contemplative.
That ruined tower staring at the horizon, with
Crows drifting, black floaters in your bad eye,
Was security against distraction and invasion.

In the first westerly gale you felt your error.
Nothing was safe in that roiling blast,
Illusions went the same way as the trees;
The sea flung fierce spray-tipped arms
Up over the rocks, snatching at the shore;
The noise made it impossible to think.

Sinking roots into the ground, you hoped,
Would keep you planted against storms:
Dirt underneath the nails and honest toil.
But little grew in the acid soil, just beets
And cabbages; who can live on those?
You began to long for an unbent back.

We met to chat on your return, your eyes
Scuttering away from mine, your voice low
And harried. "The wind has got inside my head.
The island came home with me," is what you said.

51. Leaving Luskentyre
by Gill Terry

They say late June is best
when curlews call
and ground seashell on ancient peat
fires rainbow colours through the sweet machair.
Emerald waves unfurl on an endless beach
brilliant against red Harris hills.

But we prefer mid-March
when squally showers play tug of war
with blessed bursts of sun.
Frosted jade against a pewter sky
breakers thunder and lash the shore.
This is no time for picnics
but on these shining sands
where freezing rain soothes the salty backwash
ours are the only footprints.

Back home
to see us through the year
we try in vain to reproduce the colour scheme
in photographs and watercolours,
even in the paint we choose for bedroom walls.
No matter. Until next time

we have our precious pebbles
relocated to the window sill
and in the footwell of the car
a sprinkling of white sand
we do not sweep away.

52. An Tilleadh
by Maoilios Caimbeul

1.

'S e turas anama a th' ann an eilean,
Seasaidh e leis fhèin ann am meadhan a' chuain,
Cinnteach gu bheil e ann
Seach gu bheil a' mhuir bhog ceithir thimcheall air.
Fairichidh e na tuinn a' bualadh
Latha as dèidh latha,
Air a chuairteachadh le eileanan eile
Bho Rubha Rothanais gu Maol na h-Obha.
'S e aisling a th' ann an eilean,
Fairichidh e an teas a' tighinn
Bho bhroinn na talmhainn fada shìos
Agus atharraichidh e beag air bheag,
Clach air chloich, creag air chreig.
'S tha a' mhuir an-còmhnaidh na samhla
Air saoghal fada thall, ach a tha tighinn
Am fagas, tonn às dèidh tonn.
Agus an aisling eile, tìr-mòr, a' tarraing a' ghille
A bha air an eilean – gealladh, beatha,
Solais dhathte, saorsa bho chuingean:
Fàgaibh na caoraich agus an crodh,
Agus sitig na craite agus thigibh,
A   chreutairean bochda, thugamsa
Agus blaisibh mo bhiadh blasta,

Mo ghleadhraich, mo bhùithtean mòra,
Mo sholais dheàlrach, feise air oitir.

2.

Chuimhnich an gille an t-eilean, mar a bha e:
A' cheàrdach sa Chlachan mionaid bhon taigh,
Lachaidh a' dèanamh crùidh eich,
Dearg-gheal, dìreach a-mach às a' ghrìosaich
Agus i air an innean aige 's e ga slaiceadh
Dhan chumadh cheart. 'S an t-each glas
A' feitheamh taobh a-muigh an darais.
Gobha fèitheach a chuireadh fùirneis a dhol
Leis a' bhalg-shèididh, a dhèanamh clobha
No pòcair no geata no uidheam iarainn,
Agus 's dòch', a shinnsear, nuair a bhiodh feum,
claidheamh.

'S e coimhearsnachd shlàn a bh' anns an àite,
Coimhearsnachd Ghàidhealach na craite,
Gun telebhisean air a thighinn no fiu's fòn,
Ach ann an taigh no dhà. Ach na dorsan fosgailte
Airson nàbaidh a thighinn a chèilidh. Gean
Agus gàire, 's a' gabhail naidheachd a chèile.
Bùth anns gach baile: Bùth Hatch ri ar taobh
Sa Chlachan, 's Bùth Chiorstaidh, a reiceadh suiteis,
'S ann an Steinnseal Bùth Bhertie air a h-ùr thogail

'S Bùth Sìneag aig bonn bruthach Bhrògaig,
Is Buth Henna 's Ghlas Pheighinn – reic is ceannach,
Crac is còmhradh.

Obair an fhearainn aig a fhreumh, crodh
Agus caoraich agus cearcan aig a h-uile duine,
Cha mhòr, agus san iodhlainn cruachan feòir
Agus arbhair, 's aig an taigh, cruach-mhòna.

'S bha an eaglais ann, ris na chuir e cùl,
Ann an teis-meadhan a' bhaile,
Ann an teis-meadhan iomadh cridhe,
Ach thrèig an gille i 's dh'fhalbh e
'S cha do thill airson bliadhnaichean mòra.

3.
Tha an t-eilean a' toirt cumadh air an anam
Agus an t-anam a' toirt a chumadh fhèin
Air an eilean. E an-còmhnaidh a' feitheamh
Ris an dìlleachdan tilleadh, 's tillidh e,
Cho cinnteach ris a' bhàs, no rona sin,
Nuair a dh'fhairicheas an neach-allaban
An criomadh: *Till, tha d' eilean gad ghairm*
Agus tillidh e mar an t-iasg air a thilgeil air cladach
No mar mhìr meatailt chun na cloich-iùil,
Mar Odysseus a' tilleadh gu Ithaca

Às dèidh saoghal mòr an eòlais,
Agus air ais air an eilean, coimheadaidh e suas
Air na reultan agus ionnsaichidh e nach eil
Fios aige air dad nach robh ann bho thùs
Ann an aodainn a dhaoine fhèin.

Ach tha fios aig an eilean: seallaidh e suas
Agus chì e clàr-gine na cruinne-cè
A' gluasad tro na dubh-linntean suthainn,
A' tàrmachadh mean air mhean, tonn air thonn,
Mar gum biodh a h-uile sìon
Air a cho-òrdanachadh bho thùs.

Agus chì e gu bheil na dorsan fosgailte
Fhathast, doras na h-eaglais' fhèin,
Agus thèid e a-staigh, le moladh air a bheul.

52. The Return
by Myles Campbell

1.
An island is a soul journey,
It stands on its own in the middle of the sea,
Sure of its existence
Because the soft waters completely surround it.
It feels the pressure of the waves
Day after day,
Surrounded by other islands
From the Butt of Lewis to the Mull of Oa.
An island is a dream,
It feels the heat coming up
From the depth of the earth far below
And it changes little by little,
Stone by stone, rock by rock.
And the sea is always a symbol
Of a world far beyond, but which
Approaches, wave upon wave.
And the other dream, the mainland, attracted the boy
Who was on the island – promise, life,
Bright lights, freedom from ties:
Leave the sheep and the cows,
And the midden of the croft and come,
You poor souls, to me

And taste my delicious foods,
My tumult, my big shops,
My brilliant lights, secretive sex.

2.
The boy remembered the island, how it was:
The Clachan smithy a minute from the house,
Lachlan making a horse's hoof,
White-red, just out of the fire.
He has it on the anvil, striking it
To give it the right shape. The grey horse
Is waiting outside the door.
A muscular smith who could get a furnace going
With the bellows, could make tongs
Or poker or gate or iron tool,
And perhaps, his ancestor, when it was needed,
A sword.

It was a whole community in the place,
A Gaelic crofting community,
Television not having come, or even the telephone,
Except in a house or two. But there was an open door
For a neighbour to come visiting. Humour
And laughter, and exchange of each other's news.
A shop in every township: Hatch's Shop beside us
In Clachan, and Kirsty's, which sold sweets,

And in Stenscholl Bertie's newly-built
And Sìneag's at the foot of Brogaig brae
And Henna's in Glasphein – selling and buying,
Chat and conversation.

The main thing was working the land, everyone,
Almost, with cattle and sheep and hens
And in the stackyard stacks of hay
And corn, and at the house a peatstack.

The church was there, which he rejected,
In the very middle of the village,
In the middle of many a heart,
But the boy abandoned it and he left
And didn't return for many a long year.

3.
The island shapes the soul
And the soul gives the island
Its own shape. It always waits
For the orphan's return, and he will return,
As sure as death, or before it,
When the wanderer feels the nibble:
Come back, your island is calling you
And he returns like a fish thrown on the shore
Or like a metal fragment drawn to the magnet,

Like Odysseus returning to Ithaca
After the great world of learning,
And back on the island, he looks up
At the stars and he learns that he knows
Nothing he didn't know from the beginning
In the faces of his own people.

But the island knows: it looks up
And it sees the genome of the universe
Moving through the deep time of aeons,
Originating little by little, wave by wave,
As if everything was
Co-ordinated from the beginning.

And he sees that the doors are still
Open, even the church doors,
And he goes in, and praises Heaven then.

53. The Wall
by Cait Wooll

The wire fence marks the border between one croft and another. What I think is funny is that this wire fence, rolled out from a big bundle that now sits discarded a few metres away, has been erected against a dry stone wall or 'dyke'. Currently, the sheep can climb the dry stone wall, walk along the top, and jump off into the next croft. Come time for the fanks, they not only have to be herded up as usual but then also sorted out according to their painted markings. This takes more time and means more work for the dogs. So instead of repairing the dips and gaps in the dry stone, returning it to its sheep-proof glory, some crofters have run the wire fence all the way alongside it. The wire fence is the same height as the now-damaged stone wall. Unlike the stone wall, the wire fence will rust in the rain. It will shake and warp in the gales that start in October and blow through till March. The stonewall will slowly develop more chinks and will crumble slightly in some places. No one will repair it, because old Kenny John is the one who does dry stone, and he's over on the mainland now, and besides it might work out a wee bit more money.

Having made my way up the well-trodden path I look out over the valley, the peaked roof of the medieval church sharp against the brightening sky. Our house stands out, crisp white, like an egg nestled between the hill and the water. Ahead of me the sea loch widens into the Atlantic, the Isle of Skye appearing to levitate just above the horizon. To my right the sun is making a tentative show, peering through the clouds above the Sound and turning the little islands a deep emerald. As always, I wish I'd brought my camera. Though the rain has stopped the stone wall is still slightly damp, sparkling a bit in the fresh light. Heavy rain and water running down the slope is no match for the wall; dry stone drains rapidly and dries in the wind and the sun. I rub my fingers along the wire fence and they come away greasy and brown. A few feet away, five sheep meander up to the fence/stone wall. The leader stops and looks at me. I baa and he baas loudly back, used to humans around him. He snuffles the wire fence then rubs his muzzle hard on the grass. He looks back at his friends and they fall into a single file line behind him. He stands on his hind legs, front hooves nearly to the top of the wall. With a push, his front half is up and he scrabbles with his back hooves, finding the rungs of the wire fence and using them like a ladder. He stands on top of the wall and shakes his fleece, gazing out over the sea and looking quite regal. Then he baas at his friends and one by one they follow suit. I laugh and call Goodbye to them as they trot off across the next croft, stubby tails waving. The fence is slightly crumpled where they went over, to my eyes heavy and slackened with defeat. If the wall were repaired to its former height, Sheep and his friends wouldn't be able to jump on it. In the fence they have the livestock equivalent of a footstool.

Leaning on the wall, I look up and down the length of it. The first few feet are a deep slate grey and encrusted with shells, covered regularly in Atlantic high tide. These smaller, flatter stones seem birthed by the beach, and as the wall ascends there is grass growing up its sides so that it appears rooted, emerging from the earth and rising like a prehistoric spine across the hills. Some immense slumbering creature about to sit up. That always used to scare me a little, as a child, and when we walked up the hill he used the wall as a natural handrail while I kept a safe distance, eyes peeled for any sudden shift or shake that could indicate a waking. He noticed my apprehension and I told him about the creature and without any hint of mocking he stuck his cigar in the side of his mouth, picked me up under the arms and sat me on the wall, and I sucked in my breath and waited for something momentous. Nothing happened. See, he said, puffing smoke, nothing that big will be bothered by someone so tiny. I don't know, I said, what if I surprise it? Hmm, he said, good point. Well, how about as we walk along it, we give it a bit of a pat? He walked a few steps, running his hand along the stones. I hopped off the wall and did the same, bumping my palm along the cool vertebrae. Just a nice pat, he said, to reassure it. To say, It's alright. Don't get up. Go back to sleep.

Now, today, I boost myself onto the wall, swing a leg over and sit astride. I say hello to it, out of habit. He told me it was built sometime in the 1300s. My mind circles that, a time so far away and so distant from mine, in which people stacked a wall of stones, without mortar or concrete, that would stand for seven hundred years. I imagine men and women all in a line, carefully placing the chosen rocks into an interlocking, steadfast stack. Under my palm the stone is smooth, warm with the memories of seven centuries and all the hands that built them. Hands pressing back against mine. We were here. Rain whips their medieval clothing and the rocks are slick and heavy but they keep working, because the wall needs to be there and they know exactly what they're doing. And then a few weeks ago, so-and-so parked his van in our lane and he and two others went up the hill and ran a shitty, flimsy wire fence along the length of the stone wall. It must be horrible, I say to the wall, to see yourself crumbling like this. To see everything around you do the same.

I am homesick for a person, for a place that doesn't

exist anymore.

I belong to somewhere, but somewhere is gone.

And to people, to someone, but that someone has disappeared, and so will everyone else.

It's terrifying that my brain will be the only container for him. Crack my skull like a boiled egg. Flip the top off.

I want something I can grab, hold in my hand, but even staring at my hand, turning it over, I just see it empty, picture it older, thinner, my freckled crepe-y skin draped over bone.

Then just bones, still and silent as stone, the ring finger snatched away by a fox or a mink, taken through damp, glistening green grass to a cool, dark home. Dropped, gnawed on and savoured, held in small russet paws under a grinning russet snout.

I'm horrified by what I had, grabbed hold of and lost anyway. By this thing I will   always want, rarely find and can never keep. I cannot, laughing and joking, run wire alongside this.

I've been up and down these hills a thousand times since he first brought me over. I can see myself at three, at eight, at ten after Granny died when he and I went for a walk up here, patting the wall as we ambled along, and he started crying, very quietly, looking out over the Sound, and instinctively I reached out and held his big hand with my little one, something I would hesitate to do now, to anyone, but didn't hesitate at all to do then. Neither of us said anything and eventually he took his hankie from his jacket pocket and blew his nose, squeezed my hand and then dropped it, and we walked back to the house like nothing had happened. He told me later that was the most comforting thing anyone had done since she died. Just silence and the pressure of a hand. I rarely do anything like that, hug someone or take a hand, even though there have been plenty of times I should have. So I remember that and then being twelve, in charge of our sheep for the first time, when I discovered that they liked the sound of singing. So I would go to the bottom of the croft and start something from Les Mis and all the sheep would come running from all over the hill and follow me single file as I walked to the feed shed, a white line snaking up the purpled winter hill. Mom told me later that he watched this routine every day, that he went to the window as soon as I started down the lane in my oversized wellies. She said he'd open the window and that even when we were out of sight he'd leave it open and sit smoking and snatches of my singing would drift into the house, picked up on the wind and carried across the valley.

I half-heartedly hum One Day More and my eyes follow the footsteps of Sheep and friends. Down the steeper side of the hill lies a cluster of black-houses and a rock beach. The black-houses are in ruins, the roofs and doors gone for decades and the dry stone walls now beginning to crumble. The houses are in a clever location, cuddled by hills with a point extending out into the sea like a long green finger, pointing to Skye, curving slightly to create a sea loch. An ideal place to drop anchor or pull a boat up onto the beach. I can imagine them landing here, looking around, nodding. The hills shelter the houses from the worst of the winds, and the point distils a wild sea before its waves can batter the beach. Not that this matters now, with the houses long empty and the loch devoid of boats. But if I squint, if I tilt my head just so, I can for a flash see it all. The thatched roofs, black from the smoke of the peat fire smouldering always inside. Women in shawls coming over the hill, hunched, more peat strapped to their backs. Boats sidling into the loch, shouted greetings. Far more sheep. Always fascinated by history, he gave me book after book about the island, from the Vikings through to the last lord.

Slipping forward in time, I can see the history he wrote, the things he described to me from the War. Girls in bobbed hair and tea dresses hanging washing behind their homes along the west coast. Our house still a school, the sitting room filled with rows of desks and those desks filled with fidgety children, tapping lace-up boots on scrubbed wooden floorboards. Ears attuned for the distant hum of plane engines. Deafened by the sudden, shuddering groan of them.

Past our house I can see the feed shed, past that, the hotel and the harbour. I remember being fifteen and adjusting my walk to a snail's pace so he could accompany me up the hill to feed the sheep. He loved The Finale and so I tried to draw it out but ended up just singing it four times over. Each time I finished that last line that Fantine, Eponine and Valjean sing all together he'd smile to himself and murmur, Ah, amazing. I mixed grain pellets while he kept the fattest sheep out of the shed, menacing them with his walking stick. I was stationed here for months, he told me, scrunching my favourite's fleece in his fingers. He lit a cigar and looked around, out over the sea, up at the sky. We had dances right here where this shed is. And that washing line, he pointed towards the hotel's back garden, well, there isn't one now, but there was, see how the garden sits on that slope? Morag would be hanging out sheets and things, and she always did this around the same time every day, and if I was doing checks I'd fly up this way, stay low, dangerously low to the water, tight to the side of the island, and I'd come in against the wind so she didn't hear the plane, and then I'd WOOOSH, bank and fly right up over the garden. Metres from that roof. She'd shriek and throw herself onto the grass. Scared the shit out of her

278

every time, and anyone in the hotel. Then she'd look up and see it was me and start running up the garden after the plane, arms flailing, Damn it, Gerry! And I'd wave... he mimed a wave, snickering, I'd wave and fly off back to the base. He grinned. Or maybe circle back. Do it again...he trailed off and gazed out to sea, smoke hanging like a veil in the damp air, mingling with his beard. It's all pretty clear, still, he said. But it'll go. It all goes after a while.

And see sitting on the wall, now, I wish it would go. Looking out over all this, these places, homes, this space. Teeming with space, space once moved through by people. People I don't know, ones I do know, everyone everywhere for ever will see those around them disappear. See the places they occupied disappear. I look at the feed shed and see buckets filled with pellets, feel drizzle and soft muzzles pushing against my knees. He looked at the same thing and saw himself at twenty-five playing pranks on his friends, felt the flimsy wooden plane creaking under his boots, the drone shaking his throat. White sheets flapping against blue sky and a wake of flattened grass. We looked at this wall and saw history, a feat of engineering. A cured childhood fear. Others saw something old, not worth repairing. A fank dragging into the evening.

I stood beside him at the viewing and saw folded

hands become alien, saw *know* slip into knew.

I drove clenching the wheel, mom beside me, asking frantic questions and yelling 'What?! I can't hear you!' down the phone.

I ran up stone steps half an hour too late, into a room full of people and something empty in the bed, a slowly cooling space under a duvet.

I smelled the smell of coming full circle, returning to a dim dirt hole with soft   russet paws and smiling russet snout.

I saw mom slump onto a chair and knew she smelled it too.

I said But it was the traffic. The shitty tourists, the single-track road.

Arms squeezed me and Morag, eyes drooping, said, He asked where you were, and a nearing drone began in my ears. She said, He asked a few times, he asked when you'd be here. And a chasm yawned open beside me. It gapes, slack like a broken jaw, just to the right and back. It waits patiently now while I sit on our wall.

I can't see it, but I hear it sometimes, murmuring on fetid breath, He asked where you were.

Now, today, I sit on the wall looking down at this house that's mine and the space inside and know it is not the same place I have come home to before. It and I are unanchored, drifting out, until I find something solid. I can come to places we went to before. I can let good memories come rushing in, but cannot imbue them with anything but grief. I can press my palms down on the top of our wall, like I am now; I can't think anything besides things he's told me. Give me a topic we didn't talk about, a story he didn't tell me. My entire view has been shaped by him and now I wish for new eyes.

54.   **Island Life Sentences**
       by Mary Robinson

herd old engines, pretending not to notice when they
turn feral
accept that everything you take to an island stays on an
island

find butterfly orchids mating behind the supermarket
love the moonlit sea's grey silk and not want to live
anywhere else

have a portfolio of part-time employments
skype your children who are far far away

hear a corncrake when you step off the plane
watch an otter when you had no intention of watching
otters

say in June that the winter storms are worth it for the
simmer dim
curse February for it is the longest month of all

grow up knowing you have to leave
leave knowing you have to return

biographies

Mark O. Goodwin was born in Devon and moved to Skye in 1994. He has co-authored the collection *Dà Thaobh a' Bhealaich/The Two Sides of the Pass* and is represented in the anthology *These Islands, We Sing*, Polygon 2011. He was awarded Special Merit in the National Galleries of Scotland *Inspired? Get Writing!* competition in 2013.

Val Fellows trained as an artist and art therapist, but has always been involved with creative writing.Now a permanent Skye resident she continues her art practice which incorporates her writing.

Susie Southall has settled in Sleat where she works, writes occasional verse and music, walks and often just looks out of the window.

Winner of the 2012 Baker Prize for English poetry, **Deborah Moffatt** was born in Vermont, and lives in Fife. Her first collection of poetry, "FAR FROM HOME" (Lapwing; Belfast) was published in 2004. She has published prose as well as poetry in a wide variety of journals and anthologies, and her poem "Along the Coast" was included in "Poems of the Decade" from Forward/Faber (2011).

Martin Cathcart Froden(1978) has been shortlisted for various awards, including the Bridport Prize and the Rubery Award, and longlisted for the Bristol Short Story Prize and BBC Radio 4's Opening Lines. He is currently in talks with publishers regarding his first novel. He also has a publishing deal with Sony/Imperial in Sweden for lyrics. Originally from Sweden, he has lived in Canada, Israel, Argentina and London and worked as a drummer, avocado picker, sound engineer, greengrocer and magazine editor. He now lives in Glasgow with his wife and two children.

Winner of the 2012 Baker Prize for English prose, **Juliet Lamb** was Born in England and raised in the United States, Juliet has also lived in various parts of North and South America and (most recently) Orkney, where she spent two years tracking seabirds for the RSPB. She is currently a PhD student in Wildlife

Conservation, researching Brown Pelicans in the Gulf of Mexico. The main reason she is a seabird biologist is because lighthouse-keeping is no longer a career option. Besides catching birds, she spends most of her time playing the French horn, taking photos, and writing, and recently completed a novel that may never see the light of day.

Alison Barr was born in Mayfield, near Edinburgh. She has lived and worked on the West Coast of Scotland for many years, teaching in Primary Schools. She has also lived in France, Spain and Australia. Alison has always enjoyed poetry and likes playing with words to create fresh images and ideas. Culture, landscapes and wildlife are her main inspirations. Alison is a successful Baker Prize poet.

Ian Stephen's first book of poems was published in Denmark in 1983. Recent maritime poems in 2013 Oxford Poets international anthology. His first novel (only about 30 years in making) now accepted: 'A Merry Book of Death and Fish'. www.ianstephen.co.uk. Ian is a highly successful Baker Prize poet.

Lorn Macintyre, novelist, short story writer and poet, was born in Taynuilt, Argyll, and spent formative years on the island of Mull, the inspiration for two collections of short stories, *Tobermory Days* and *Tobermory Tales*. His poetry collection, *A Snowball in Summer*, was published in 2009. He has had a lifelong interest in the paranormal, in particular in its relation to the creative imagination. He has worked for BBC Scotland on cultural television programmes. His website is at www.lornmacintyre.co.uk

Andy Jackson is from Manchester but moved to Fife twenty years ago. His poems have appeared in Magma, Blackbox Recorder and Trespass. He is editor of 'Split Screen' (Red Squirrel 2012), an anthology of film & TV poetry. His debut collection 'The Assassination Museum' was published by Red Squirrel in 2010. An historical anthology of Dundee poetry entitled 'Whaleback City' co-edited with WN Herbert was published in 2013. Andy is a successful Baker Prize poet, winning 1st, 3rd and 'highly acclaimed' in the English poetry section.

Jen Hadfield is a highly accomplished poet. Her second collection, *Nigh-No-Place*, won the 2008 T S Eliot Prize. With family in Canada and England and a deep love of her adopted home in Shetland, it is perhaps no surprise that her writing is often drawn to the contradictions of travel and home, the music of voices, and the importance of land and place.

Morag Henriksen, a Ross from Ross-shire, grew up in Lochcarron, was a teacher in Edinburgh, Portree and Uig. An artist, writer, poet and singer, she has lived on the Isle of Skye since 1967 and has two sons, Ross and Scott, both artists.

Kevin MacNeil is a Scottish novelist, poet and playwright born and raised in the Outer Hebrides. His novels, A Method Actor's Guide to Jekyll and Hyde and best-selling debut, The Stornoway Way, were both published to widespread critical acclaim. Kevin is a long time supporter of the Skye Reading Room.

Drew Love Jones grew up in a farming family in deepest Englandshire. While not breaking machinery he could usually found grubbing about in a pond or hedge bottom. This gave him a deep and abiding interest in the countryside and its inhabitants. Only comparatively recently has he discovered that writing is for more than cheques and shopping lists and now when he is not doing nasty things to trees can usually be spotted pecking away at a keyboard. He is absolutely chuffed to be included.

Sùsaidh Arnold has written occasional poems throughout her life but only had two published, one in 1965 and another in 1997. However, since moving to Skye in 2001, learning Gaelic and now being retired, she enjoys creative writing in Gaelic. She is grateful for the encouragement of Catriona Lexy Caimbeul at her Sabhal Mòr Ostaig writing group.

Richard Neath is co-founder of the Skye Reading Room. He has written two novels *A Fall of Stone (2003) and Breakfast Will Do (2012)* and is a regular contributor to *Waterlog*, the world's leading literary angling magazine. He lives and works on Skye with his wife and two beagles. No matter what he's doing, he would almost certainly rather be writing or fishing or writing *about* fishing. Or even writing *whilst* fishing. www.richardneath.com

Garry MacKenzie has a Masters in Creative Writing from the University of St Andrews, and is now studying for a PhD in Landscape in Modern Poetry. Originally from Glasgow, he lives in Crail, Fife. Garry achieved 2nd place in the 2012 Baker Prize, English poetry.

Catriona Lexy Campbell is from the Isle of Lewis and has worked in her native Gaelic as a writer, actor and theatre artist for many years. She has published several books including *Cleasan a Bhaile Mhòir* (Sandstone Press, 2009), *Samhraidhean Dìomhair* (Comunn na Leabhraichean, 2009) and *Cluicheadaran* (Acair, 2013). She was the Writer in Residence at Sabhal Mòr Ostaig in 2013.

Alison Lang lives in Edinburgh and writes in both Gaelic and English. Her first collection of short fiction, *Cainnt na Caileige Caillte* (The Lost Girl's Language), was shortlisted for the Saltire Society's First Book of the Year Award. She has since published a novella, *San Dùthaich Ùir* (In the New Country), and is currently working on a new Gaelic play with the support of Playwrights' Studio Scotland, and on her first English novel. www.alisonlang.co.uk

Robin Jenkins is a gardener with a passion for building dry stane dykes. Most of his ideas come to him as he works outside and he then make use of any periods of particularly bad weather to write up and edit those ideas. He won the Imprint Writing Competition twice, took part in 'Bloody Scotland' and has had the odd story published. He's presently struggling with a thriller about the politics of drug dealers and the wider society they inhabit.

Linda Henderson lives on Skye with her husband and 'Jasper' a springer spaniel. She has been a writer for many years and is the author of many short stories and poems published in collected works such as the New Writers Scotland anthology series.

Gill Terry has always enjoyed writing though her early publications were in scientific journals. A change of careers, a move to a Scottish island and an Open University Diploma in Creative Writing and Literature have allowed her writing to follow a different path. She enjoys poetry and short fiction and considers all her best work to be 'life writing' of some sort. She has had examples published in 'Body Parts and Coal Dust', 'Club Eclectic', and 'To the Edge of There and Back', all published by The Right Eyed Deer Press.

Jane Verburg lives in Cromarty. She teaches, makes silver jewellery and is involved with wildlife surveys. Her short stories and poems are inspired by local history and landscape. Her work has been acknowledged in numerous competitions, including The Neil Gunn and The Baker Prize Competitions. She won the Sir Thomas Urquhart Writing Competition with a story for primary school pupils. She regularly writes book reviews for 'Northwords Now' and has been published in 'Coast' magazine. Jane and her husband are keen sailors and in summer they explore the northwest islands in their wee sailing boat with their sausage dog.

Maureen MacKenzie was born in Glasgow, the oldest of eight children and has lived in Heatherfield, in the Braes area, for the last twenty two years. She has a daughter and two sons and has worked as a civil servant, registrar and primary teacher.
This piece is based on the boat building shed which was last used by her father-in-law, although he died about twenty years before she moved to Skye. It is a place she has always loved which was brought to life by her mother-in-law's oral history of the family and vivid recollections.

Mary Robinson lives in the north Cumbria within sight of the Scottish hills. Her collection *The Art of Gardening* was published in 2010 by Flambard Press. It includes poems about the Hebrides, Orkney and Shetland. A pamphlet *Uist Waulking Song* was published in 2012 by Westward Books. She is the winner of the 2013 Mirehouse Poetry Prize. She writes a literary blog *Wild About Poetry* at http://maryrobinsonpoetry.blogspot.com

S.A. Kelly was born on the thirteenth in the Shire of Ayr. She is not a witch. She currently lives between the islands of Skye and North Uist, and, when not writing, spends her time recovering from M.E./CFS and studying Scottish Cultural Studies through the University of the Highlands and Islands. Her writing uses fantasy and Scottish folklore to explore and rationalise the darker parts of everyday life.

Originally from Kilmarnock, **Heather Marshall** is currently based in the foothills of South Carolina. Her work is published in a variety of periodicals in the US and the UK. *Kaolin* is part of a collection of short stories for which Heather is currently seeking publication. *Payline* is part of a collection of linked short fiction and creative nonfiction based on Heather's adoption and reunion. Her first novel, *The Thorn Tree,* will be published in late 2013. Heather won the inaugural Baker Prize (English prose) and achieved 2nd place in the 2012 competition also.

Thomas Rist is Senior Lecturer in the Department of English at the University of Aberdeen. When work allows, he writes and even occasionally publishes poetry, as for example in *Poetry Scotland* (2007),*Northwords* (2009) and *Causeway* (2010). His poem 'Cairn' won the *Scottish Mountaineer* poetry prize of 2005 and in 2010 his 'The Leafblowers' received a commendation in the annual competition of the poetry journal *Rubies in the Darkness*. 'On the Bikini Atoll' is one of a number of poems Thomas wrote while recovering from cancer.

Natasha Yapp is an Edinburgh-based writer of poetry, blogs and stand-up comedy.
'His Island Life' has been a work in progress for the last 2 years or so, and she has written several different versions of the poem. In this short work, some of the themes she attempts to convey are, in her opinion, quite typical of the harsher aspects of island life. These include isolation, loss, alienation, and feeling "foreign" to an island's culture.

Charlotte Johnson was a regular visitor to Skye before moving here in 2008. She runs a busy B&B in Portree and in her 'spare' time, is Chair of the Reading

Room, produces and presents the Reading Room Show on the local radio station CuillinFM and occasionally finds time to write.

Liz Shaw but spent her childhood and much of her adult life in England. However she has always felt a close link with her Highland roots since spending all her summer holidays on the island with her grandparents. She was always aware of how the history of Skye was as tangible yet as elusive as the frequent mists. After years of Skye being the other place she visited as often as possible, she's now fortunate to be able to call it her home .
Her debut novel 'Love and Music Will Endure' is due for launch at the end of 2013.

Peter Mackay is a successful writer, broadcaster, academic & Journalist. He has produced highly acclaimed works on subjects such as Sorely MacLean, Gaelic and Irish literature.

John Maguire worked in the chemical industry, and then as a university lecturer. On retirement, he joined a writing group, before completing a Masters' degree in creative writing at Newcastle University. He lives in the Tyne Valley. He has spent much rewarding time in the North of Scotland and the islands of the Hebrides, rock-climbing, walking and cycling.

Ruth Aylett teaches computing in Edinburgh and her poetry takes up the personal, the political and the scientific. She has been published in anthologies by Red Squirrel Press, Estuary, Doire Press and Blind Poetics and has read as a Shore Poets New Poet. In Summer 2012 she appeared in the Inky Fingers Minifest in Edinburgh with Sarah the Poetic Robot. You can read more about her writing at www.macs.hw.ac.uk/~ruth/writing.html.

Maoilios Caimbeul (Myles Campbell) is a Gaelic poet and writer who lives in Skye. His mother was from Staffin and his father from Ness in Lewis and he was brought up in the islands and the west coast of Scotland. His latest work includes *Island Conversion*, co-authored with his wife Margaret. A new poetry collection is expected from Clàr in 2014 and a new children's illustrated novel from Acair, both in Gaelic. Myles is a long time friend and supporter of the Skye Reading Room.

Caitlin Wooll was born in Niagara on the Lake, Ontario, Canada. Her grandfather flew in the RAF during WWII and was stationed for a time in Stornoway, Isle of Lewis. He later bought a house on the Isle of Harris and took his family there on yearly trips. Cait went to the University of Glasgow for both an MA(Hons) and an MLitt, then moved to Harris for the beaches, mountains and a job that has nothing to do with her degree.